My Summer Vacation

Tom Levine

Defiant Worm Books

Notfiction

ISBN 9729390-2-4

First Commercial Edition
First Printing

Printed in Florida

Order books at defiantworm.weebly.com

Praise received at defiantworm@yahoo.com

Text arranged by Once More Unto the Page Formatting

Invaluable technical support and printing by Thunderbird Press

But wait! There's more -

Bite Me! Tom Levine's Most Excellent Stories
Paradise Interrupted
Bass Fishing in Outer Space and Other Stories
The Last Opus of Hector Berlioz
The Light of a Day's Metallic

My Summer Vacation

begins ….

NOW!

Author's Note

Most readers enjoy stories they can relate to or that may someday help them. This probably is neither. Press on anyway because you never know when you'll want to get some shut-eye at an elephant party. I certainly didn't expect it.

A Timely Note

My four and a half months in Africa felt like a year and a half, so it was quite a bargain – four for the price of one. I suggest you take at least the calendar period to read about it. To get the real feel, go for the year and a half. With any luck it'll feel like six. Better yet, close this thing before page 70 and head to that wonderful place yourself. Do it your way. Read this after you get back and we'll compare notes.

1

Who ever had an amazing trip because it went exactly as planned? Consider Shackleton. His worst nightmare immortalized him by turning the latest slog to the South Pole into one humdinger of an adventure. Suppose he got there like he intended to: "Enh. Yawn. Did it, just like I said we would. Looks like the rest of the bloody place. We'll have a spot of tea, take some Kodaks, urinate on the Norwegian flag and bugger off to the Ross Sea." All nod and grunt in agreement. What a loss that would have been for the history of the human spirit; but a different trip was in store as the leader naively walked out his front door and headed for the Endurance. "Ernest," the planet would coo by way of crushing his ship in the pack-ice like Smokey Bear with a match box, "the South Pole's boring. I'm going to show you what you're capable of."

The fact is we're all this guy, with instincts lain dormant under artificial lives. Only by exiting or getting knocked out of our man-made comfort zones can we escape what we're expected to do and find out what we can really do. Here's some advice for your journey of self destru...er, discovery:

Look for the bear necessities
The simple bear necessities
Forget about your worries and your strife
I mean the bear necessities
That's why we all can rest at ease
With just the bear necessities of life.

Or you could go with...

You load sixteen tons, what do you get?
another day older and deeper in debt
Saint Peter don't you call me
'cause I can't go...
I owe my soul to the company store...

It seems we're chronically torn between those two songs. I suggest you skip alongside Balloo and me and bearly prepare because it's easier that way, more flexible and cheaper. Resist remote controlling yourself, setting from here what you'll do there. This kills spontaneity dead as disco and with it your shot at immortality. Conspire only with the planet because the more you pay other people for your trip, the less yours it will be. Just start moving toward a destination and hope you never make it, letting the world surprise you with coming events. You can always get there next time.

There you have it. Set out tomorrow. The less you plan, the more it will work out unless you're an astronaut. Astronauts find a dearth of options between A and B. Better just get to B and then back to A. Then again, look at Apollo 13. Who remembers number 12 ?

That's all the advice you'll find in this book. The remaining words are dedicated to backing it up, although it may not always appear that way. For the skeptical I recommend patience.

Special note: The reader must have noticed that I almost wrote "self destruction" up there. I left it in because this is an honest narrative and for some strange reason that was my initial impulse. You can decide for yourself if there's anything to it.

So - the best laid plans of men at least, can't compete with all the rest. In the United States and Europe, zero plans worked for me like a magic potion so in 1981 I took it to East Africa - get to the correct side of the ocean and see what happens next. Plenty of that turned up with a lot more on the line. What little I envisioned evaporated and left room for far better; and worse. How much better and worse I couldn't have dreamed, lacking anything to dream it with.

Good luck awaits those who expect it and there's acres of that unless you're Eckaru Wallis, who couldn't trip over it blindfolded. Maybe he didn't expect to. Without it I wouldn't have come near surviving my clueless journey on the Dark Continent, the culmination of this story.

How I got this way –

I was supposed to be a rich kid. And naturally after that, a rich grown-up. There, I've said it. Started out that way, fancy friends, big Spanish style house on an acre of Long Island, priced over a million today on Zillow, Sid Caesar down the street; Dad's in a bar with a drink and Sinatra sits next to him, Hi, Francis. I shoulda been travelin' first class, not worst class; Club Med, pricey hotels, purely upper crust, not car with rust, give to charity, not be one.

That future followed the dodo's before I could glimpse it. The money went away and my parents were dispossessed of what they had mistaken for their lifelong abode and lifestyle. I recall my mother's frustration at lacking time even to sell our excellent furniture for a decent price.

Surprise pregnant at 39 and twenty years her husband's junior, Mom took my sister and me to stay with her Aunt Violet in a little white frame house in Apopka, Florida 1958, whites only drinking fountains, the Three K's, and "nigger" the parlance of the day. We came to reconstruct our lives where Reconstruction itself had barely a toe-hold. Because our black housekeeper in New York was like family, my eight-year old self didn't tolerate prejudice. If some hick said nigger or jigaboo, he was calling Maude one; so I hit the ground correcting people's language. Little would she have imagined the opening of this new front.

This was the third time Dad had lost everything, each everything very distinct. When he was eight, my father made a far more daunting journey with his sister and brothers to Ellis Island, his young parents Anna and Abraham already depicted in their final photograph. In the scheme of terrible events in his life, the current one, at the moment, was only financial.

We moved 12 miles further south to then obscure Orlando where Mom got a mortgage on a modest house in a nice neighborhood and five people would learn to share one Spartan bathroom. My dad considered anywhere between Jacksonville and Miami camping out; but he grabbed a can of 6-12 and bravely jettisoned his friends and siblings to join his family, starting from scratch while Mom produced my little sister and worked as a nurse to support us. I well remember the exciting step forward when my folks were able to get an air conditioner installed on the living room wall.

Quite the astonishing turnaround; they met because Mom was a nurse and now we endured by dint of it. My sister started seventh grade and I third, consummating our dive from the best public school system in the country to one of the worst. The only thing holding Florida off rock bottom was Mississippi.

My father was born in Russia. I knew that for a fact because one day while receiving discipline in the principal's office, I glimpsed my folder and noticed it written in red ink across the front. I told my parents about that and Mom, never one to remain quiet for no reason, personally demanded its removal. They assured her it would be done. In high school I would again glimpse my folder and note that they hadn't gotten around to it yet.

I might have been a little traumatized by our family's downheaval but I don't remember. Maybe balcony-loss. I really liked the balconies. No balcony but plenty baloney. At least we still had baloney. I loved pulling the strings through my teeth. My first school day in Orlando it was black-eyed peas for lunch. No way was I putting that in my mouth so they let me sit in the cafeteria until I did and that was the rest of my first day.

My first Orlando teacher suspected I was mentally retarded and summoned the county psychologist to confirm it. He demurred and at year's end she was fired. (So, Mrs. Ogram - *now* who's out of step?) Next I was branded a "smart-mouth," which, one would think, would be a good thing. If you can't be smart, get a smart mouth and you'll at least sound like it. I was ahead of my time. Now we got smart phones, smart toilets, time for the smart mouth. Re-configures your thoughts into intelligence before anybody hears them; works for everybody but Fox News. Some things you just can't fix. And I was class cut-up, "Tommy is constantly making smart remarks to cause disturbances" - again – disparaging smart.

They called it "lack of self control." Today they call it ADHD. I call it high-spirited. Chronically in trouble, it weighed heavily on me. More than church I dreaded report card day. Every time I hoped against reason to find some hint of redemption in that brown cardboard jacket as I feverishly pulled out the indictment. The best I ever got was acknowledgment of my desperate stab at conformity in the final week of the period. Once I even flunked conduct. Mom was hoping somehow to assimilate, like the Bizarro-Clampetts, and it felt like I wasn't helping that ambitious cause.

A strong Southern Baptist artery flooded the corridors of Blankner Elementary School. The Pledge of Mindless Obedience and the Protestant version of The Lord's Prayer kicked off every mind numbing day and most of the teachers seemed loony to me. We were commanded to pray bent-necked and blind but my Catholic mother thought God should be addressed looking straight ahead with vision ("you look people in the eye when you're talking to them") so I never got it right; but the teacher's eyes were shuttered so she never knew (if one of my teachers is reading this, ha, ha!). Nor did I master the protocol of The Pledge, never giving a hoot about Richard Stanz.

One day, no doubt trying to assimilate, I said, "Go' durn it," short for "Gol' durn it." Not up on the latest contractions, Mrs. Boxall grabbed me by the shoulders and shook me against a wall screeching repeatedly, "Don't you take the name of The Lord in vain." That's what I got for trying to fit in - blasphemed against Golly, that famous creator of the universe. I did manage to incorporate the less perilous "ain't," probably so I could say "I ain't got no this" and "I ain't got no that" and later on "Ain't no Viet Cong ever called me nigger," which I never needed due to winning the lottery.

From an early age I had been considered very well spoken, at about three nicknamed The Little Professor and I recall my mother saying, "I can't believe you say 'ain't'." Now a part of family lore, I responded, "You ain't seen nothin' yet." I don't know if she was glad or sad.

Then there was Mrs. Enos, a tall, asparagus-like affair whom I never smahled at. Even though I wasn't in her class, she would grab me by the ear lobe and jerk me around cackling "Smahl at me. Smahl at me." Mom told me to respect all adults. I felt this was asking too much, resolving to treat all adults with consideration for their age and respect those who inspired it. But I kept this to myself.

It ain't like it was all bad. In fourth grade a middle aged failed opera singer had inexplicably fallen into our midst. Being our music teacher was not something she had expected to encounter before going to Hell but she pinched her nose and carried on as a ballerina might tiptoe across a stage slathered in swan guano. She steadfastly maintained an erudite demeanor before us, caht not cat, haht not hat, don't know what she said for "hot," her only apparent goal being to endure the crucible with dignity. And she might have made it but for the new arrival.

On one of these close brushes with culture she was

esoterically describing some basic aspect of music. Enter Okie, a shrunken, ragged kid with a dirty mug like he just looked up from the feeding trough and was surprised to find the world still there, recently arrived from The Grapes of Wrath. He cocks his head quizzically and says, “I don't getcha.”

And he meant it. Truer words probably were never spoke.

This outreach for clearer elucidation, Okie's brazen attempt at interspecies communication found our grand lady at the tipping point; that his brain should touch hers, one straw more than her fragile, dissolving existence would accommodate. Her placido facade twisted into a crescendo of bulbous fury. “I don't getcha?” she mimicked, projecting wonder like she was going for the deeper meaning. Sprayed hair hovering above her head, violating the opening bars of the Fidelio Overture, she shrieked the quaint statement, again as a question, and an even more alarming third time. She turned then and ran out the room blithering Okie's fateful words like a lunatic anthem, never again to be seen by us or perhaps anyone on the outside. Her visits had been no relief from the monotony and I didn't miss them.

Relief from the monotony was a day we had this substitute teacher whose uncool custom was to make us learn stuff when Golly had cut us a rare break by laying low the usual ringmaster. Getting into the swing of Florida things, I happened upon a snake outside which I brought in and offered in lieu of an apple. This treed her on top of the desk until she saw an opening and made her move. That was our last look at Mrs. Johnson and spit wads were flyin' the rest of the day with an occasional look-in from the janitor.

It wasn't any good being kind to them either. One day we got a wimpy young guy lacking the number one survival skill, the ability to bluff, and his vacuum of actual authority had been made manifest. The inmates smelled blood and spit wads were flyin' even though he was there, and flyin' at him, one splatting into his forehead. I suppose this is how revolutions start. Feeling pity, I stood and encouraged the mob to cut him some slack. Just like when John Wayne stepped between Jimmy Stewart and Liberty Valance and Stewart belted him for his trouble, the besieged sub got angry finally, at his only ally and wrote me up. I learned early that "No good deed..." adage.

Except for when I was being assaulted by a teacher and recess, confinement all day at this school was incredibly boring torture and I lived for two things – 3:00, when school let out, and the overarching paradise of summer vacation, which at its start had no conceivable end. I don't know that I ever have felt joy rivaling that emancipation. I grasped the magnitude of la difference' when I saw girls sobbing because the school year was over.

> Oh, the gallant fisher's life!
> It is the best of any;
> 'T is full of pleasure, void of strife,
> And 't is beloved by many. -
>
> Izaak Walton

I had heard the siren call of fishes and wanted always to be fishing. With ancestors from the Emerald Isle and the Black Sea, this natural urge hit me hard. Luckily lakes nestled nearby or I would have exploded or sublimated the instinct into some cheap imitation, as many do. Fishing every day after jail and all day every day all summer - that delivered me a degree of satisfaction available only through fulfillment of genetic propensity. Imagine we had fallen to Iowa! Full of fishermen raised where they oughtn't to be, trying to find their way through a corn maze with no exit. This is a problem with modern man's mobility – neuroses from having to endure outside our element.

School had devolved into nothing more than fishing time squandered. I thought only about the clock on the wall and my grades reflected that. Then here comes church to take the shine off Sunday, that forty-five agonizing minutes mostly in Latin feeling

longer than
the only kid
assured. But e
threw out basebal
successor in center
my life, had I devo
energy usurped by fishi

Mom was working t
she could be there for us in
sleep. She appreciated my l
the larder while I felt good con ... it,
it was largemouth bass every Fr ... flakes,
an invention Mom, being a child ... couldn't resist.
But sometimes I just rode my bike ... uth Dixie Highway
(now Orange Avenue in name only) a ... ar as I figured I could go and make it back by sunset, flat tire the only serious threat to freedom.

I was a tree climber, not a social climber and my true friends were Wayne Brant and Chester Peeler. Pear- shaped Wayne was one of eighteen siblings. Only in the middle of a lake could Wayne go ten minutes without some small family reunion. After ten minutes a cousin would likely go floating by. His glaringly hairless father, font of all the children with consecutive mothers, slept in a trailer off the disreputable Orange Blossom Trail and gave his waking hours to the Tick-Tock Lounge. Part of the second batch, Wayne lived with his mom and sister Twila in a small cinder block house five blocks from mine. His first car was an ivory '56 Caddy with windshield washers he customized to spray other cars when cruising Steak 'n' Shake. It threw a rod and he just kept pouring in oil and driving it like that and you always knew Wayne was coming for fifteen minutes. He would clatter by the Tick-Tock and yell over the din, "Alcoholics!" I was certain Wayne never would partake of alcohol but I was certainly wrong.

Chester and his sister Betty Sue inhabited a frame house

sewage lift station. Mrs. of encrusted dishes for whatever ed an extra one, the embedded food so couldn't use it. His mother's emissary to the bby, blonde Chester sheepishly arrived every day looking like he'd been polished, and their red-faced, eless father could belch and fart simultaneously.

They could not have been dreamt of from our previous location.

These boys may not have been high society but they had no meanness and they weren't bigots and they also loved fishing. We even formed an unholy alliance in aid of a much bullied effeminate and inoffensive classmate, vowing to intervene whenever necessary, whether together or alone. (Bullying was common and if you wanted to interject yourself, it was always the same three words – "Leave him alone," followed by the antagonist's last name or the less personal "Butthole." Then you would find out what was going to happen next.) Even so, my mother would have liked to see me branch out but I was satisfied not to. After everything went south, the normal once taken for granted no longer was in reach, or even on the horizon. Maybe Mom still saw it out there, as she had left it, missing only us, tethered to being broke in this primitive culture 1,100 miles away.

A brief look at the good old days –

This was when farting was not okay but smoking cigarets was acceptable, nay, unimpeachable behavior, any time, any place, in your face; when American women boldly asserted the right, nay, the need to appear as stupid as men. One never would ask someone to defuse his/her stink bomb. That wouldn't be Kool. But luckily I had been blessed with a talent for belching with nearly supernatural depth and power, and the righteousness to unleash it full blast whenever and wherever it was ready, especially at a smoker, without an "Excuse me." Any place, I should qualify, except the presence of my mother who would swat me with a startling reflex. This exempted church from my blessing as I never was there without her, although one did sneak up as I knelt at the Communion rail and blasted out before I could even try to muffle it. It rarely was my initiative. Like an act of God, the truly thunderous events came of their own accord, forcing open my mouth lest the skull shatter. I could only hope the offended priest was at least a Marlboro man.

Ironically that innocent protest was deemed disgusting by smokers, armored in the prevailing wind, gazing askance from atop their high horse of social acceptance; incapable of appreciating a good belch.

Racial integration arrived at my rough-and-ready junior high in the form of one innocent kid. I recall the lunch period in the dirt yard when he was surrounded by fellow students spitting on him and the smile never abandoned his face. I was ready to help if he showed the slightest annoyance but he just stood there and took it like he was sho' glad fo' the attenshun. I let him play it his way.

By the time my little sister ascended to that school, the tables had turned and she was bullied by tough black girls for being cute and white.

The benign bigot:

Mom has a nurse friend married into the old Florida citrus family Partin and they got a spread out Maitland way with a live oak branch perfect for throwin' a chain over. It's 1974 and Motorhead Mike Fioramanti and I are out there swappin' in a junkyard 318 for the blown 279 in my second car also second car to blow an engine within two weeks of me buyin' it, people keep seein' me comin'. Bob Partin has a dawg name of Stumpy, God knows why, it has all its legs and more.

Bob always reminded me of a toad. He's plopped out there with Stumpy where we're workin', like a giant bean bag with his toad face baskin' in the luxury of somebody else's problem and up walks a 12 - year old boy too young to appreciate it like Bob does, but we're the only show in town.

Bob spies him and with no introduction, just cranks open his wide, flat, toad mouth and says nice as pie, “Is they any niggers in your school?”

There's Bob, iggorant of any possible offense, not a mean bone in his toad body, tryin' to keep up with the times, jest wantin' to know if them rumors wuz true. I was pretty sure, to put it in the parlance of the day, Bob didn't mean nothin' by it.

A whole frustratin' day came that seemed like a lifetime not in the good way, I was alone under the car jackin' up and down the transmission tryin' to line up the spindle with the hole in the replacement engine, afraid, after a while, that it was impossible. Toward dark I thunk of alterin' the angle by jackin' up the engine and when it slid right in was one of the great moments of my life and ka-thunk one of the great sounds.

A week later Mike had ev'rything connected up and we discovered the 318 was frozen from sittin' and couldn't be turned over by the starter so Mike pushed it with his Chevy Malibu convertible to thirty mph and I popped the clutch in second gear. Yahoo! That broke it a-loose and then the engine caught fire and burnt up all the wiring under the hood. Thank Norman Rockwell I already had my great moment and nobody nor nothin' could take that away.

2

My twenty years older brother Arnie came from our father's original marriage. Of frail constitution, Arnie's mother Eve left him a year after his birth as they both slept, and he endured with the belief that when he took life, he took it from his mother and from his father his wife, cemented by his Aunt Rae telling him so. There instead of Mom, that's an awfully big hole for a newcomer to fill.

Eve was sibling to Earl Cohen, a prolific champion of civil rights who of necessity wrote books under the pen name Conrad. Even with the Anglicized name, white publishers wouldn't touch his civil rights books so black-owned presses published them. For The Chicago Defender he investigated rape and lynching in the south, in fact run out of Ocoee, Florida in 1950 while working on a story. A Klan wife had visited the motel and warned his wife Alyse that they would be coming for him. I have recently learned that the Orange County Sheriff then and until 1971 was very publicly a member.

I had seen Earl only once, when he defended his Billy Rose biography on the Today Show. Bumming around California in 1978, I would look up him and Alyse. They couldn't have known me from Adam but were very kind and tried to give me money. I must have seemed like some absurd addendum to Earl's former brother-in-law's life, someone not supposed to be who lived only because his sister could not. Arnie wasn't alone in taking life from his mother. Earl said the only book that made him any money was his ghostwriting of Errol Flynn's autobiography.

My future dad entrusted the baby to his in-laws who had a farm in upper state New York and gave him a grandfather and a solid chance to grow up normally; but Dad's sister Rae used the court to retrieve him from that chance, contending the Cohens were too old. Arnie moved to Manhattan to stay with his aunt and a playwright who played ball with him and other fatherly things and they bonded. Then, reeling from some bad reviews, the playwright outdid the critics in the empty theater and shot his brain. Arnie probably noticed that whenever he made the scene, somebody checked out.

My father never spoke of what he did for fourteen years before falling for the blonde beauty who would be my mom. Ridiculous as it sounds, neither synagogue nor church would bind them so it was left to a justice of the peace, just the three of them. Due to the idiotic norms of that particular time, my mother was punished for being open-minded, and denied a wedding. What a shindig it would have been.

Rae her immigrant self attended the top universities in the country and had become a psychiatrist, working for the United Nations Relief Administration. Arnie's new shot at a family was torpedoed by his aunt whose learned influence on her siblings was way disproportionate to her size and her tolerance. She venomously opposed her brother marrying a goy and never accepted it for her brother or her nephew. Arnie was sent to a military school in Georgia, then shipped out to Korea a year before I was born, qualified in sharpshooting and bazooka. He said there were two open drums on the boat over – one labeled inedible garbage. He was lucky to make it back, returned by a bogus order he himself typed up and forged shortly before most of his company was erased in a mine field. Back home he showed off his martial abilities by shooting a gopher in the yard and broke down when he saw what he'd done, vowing never to kill another thing.

There was a power, presence and indomitable intellect to my brother that, combined with his six feet and three I found intimidating. Mom used to say he was a true Leo. He also was warm, charismatic and funny, charming to people of all ages. But he was distracted by a lifelong search for his father (who had become engaged in being other peoples' father) and imbued with a potent knack for self-sabotage, never allowing himself prosperity. A little voice within would say, "Now's the time to wreck this." Even while his broad grin lit up a room, his black eyes were pleading for clemency.

With no address he came and went from our lives in Orlando, bringing joy and leaving worry. I was either missing my brother or hoping he would stay. Drawn to Manhattan, sometimes he rode the subway all night and considered following the playwright. We always wished he would turn toward the safe, usual satisfactions available to most people; like so many movie themes, that he would go straight before it was too late.

One time he showed up with a vinyl recorded by a young woman he was dating in New York, raved about her talent and what a star she was going to be; told of being in the studio when she blew away everyone by doing an entire album in one take. I remember looking at the jacket photo and being surprised my dapper brother would date someone with a schnoz like that. But he wasn't wrong. Barbra did alright. And she married a man with an address.

Arnie was a baseball fan and a schmoozer, once lunching with Mickey Mantle and Walter Winchell. Eighty-two and abed with prostate cancer at the Memphis VA hospital, he revealed to me a fascinating bit of heretofore unpublished baseball trivia - that after Don Larsen pitched the only perfect game in World Series history, it wasn't Don that the pitcher's girlfriend capped off the perfect day with. Yes, that's right. While Larsen was occupied regaling his fans, an extra-inning shot went over the center field wall.

At 37 Arnie was slain by a charming Tupelo 24 year old, another blonde goy. They were married at the open-minded Unitarian Church in Orlando. Rae wasted no time trying to wedge them apart. On meeting, her ominous greeting to Pat was, "Good luck. I'm a psychiatrist and I can't help him."

It seems her assessment was right, skilled mainly in wounding.

From the same town, Pat was a personal friend of Elvis and she did his hair on tour. She arranged for Arnie and him to spend an evening together at Graceland, just the two of them. Arnie said Elvis was very nice and down to earth, respectfully called him Arnold and showed him his belt buckle collection. Friends with Dr. Nick, Pat and Arnie evolved into staunch defenders of him. Farther along in this recap a friend of Mississippi author John Grisham is dating Arnie's now ex-wife and they all happen to meet in the check-out at Memphis Kroger's. He later told Pat that Arnie (who always charmed the cashier into feeling special) in his seventies and with little means, was the most remarkable person he'd ever met. And that surely was true. He had everything in spades except a good start in life. Could have succeeded but there was nothing requiring effort he cared to succeed at. As I grew, Mom was ever vigilant for signs I would follow suit.

But I displayed a flair for working-class and felt natural with it, even proud. I had no ambition to rise either financially or socially beyond my friends, much like Turkana tribesmen I would one day inconceivably meet, to whom Florida standards for advancement would mean very little. Rather than trying to gain influence over "the man" like the well-to-do, I felt oppression and played my role in it; to the extent that, when I did the unthinkable and ran for mayor in 2000, I dubbed it The Great Orlando Peasant Revolt, and promised, "Will be mayor for food."

The city was ruled by religious fanatics who presumed it God's will that Orlando become a "world class city," code for polluted, paved and patrolled (not one for middlemen, the incumbent spent election night alone, praying for votes in the Episcopal Cathedral). It was my will to thoroughly demolish the power structure. Though I had long since lost contact with Chester and Wayne, I would have been embarrassed for them to see this grab for power, out of loyalty to the old days.

Due to televised debates, that Quixotic effort catapulted me from obscurity into local celebrity with the twist that I was usually perceived as someone of means and influence, probably a lawyer; showing that in the public mind celebrity is not for the peasantry.

In the end I had overestimated how many voters would like to consider themselves peasants and underestimated the unethical depths to which the local daily would stoop to undercut democracy. The mayor gushed that I was sent by God not to deliver the peasants but to smite her conventional opponent in my star- crossed cause, thereby ensuring her another term for Orlando to realize its ordained destiny. Talk about foreign intervention in an election. Apparently God, patriot though She is, lacks faith in democracy. Who knew? Another side trip was the head (and other parts) of the Orange County Democrats' delusion that by enabling the Republican to remain in City Hall during the tight Florida vote count, I, not he, was responsible for George Bush's ascendancy, thus setting squarely on my shoulders blame for the Iraq attack. What an idiot. Didn't he understand I was an unwitting instrument of God?

I recall as a child hoping not to get rich because I wouldn't know who my friends really were. Thank goodness I never had to worry about that.

3

After thirteen hardscrabble years in Orlando, Dad finally caught fire in the real state business and it looked like we had some real prospects. But several months after I graduated college in '72, he succumbed to complications from smoking and the medieval treatment he received. I still can see my detached, never serious, jocular brother at his hospital bedside entirely out of character, devastated and hopeless beyond relief as the father he had just started to find drew near to leaving the field and taking the goal posts with him.

Had Dad eluded the doctors longer, probably I would have followed him into real estate. His absence seemed to set me adrift. My mother's Chicago brothers advised me individually: A very sentimental truck driver who wept over Jimmy Hoffa's disappearance while talking heads speculated (immune to all the mystery, he knew instantly that Hoffa was history), Uncle Tommy said I had to stay and take care of my mother and sisters more than ever.

Though at fourteen a "runner" for the Prohibition family business, delivering to your door, Uncle Jack never ran a step in his life, from polio. The lighthearted one, he owned a bar in Las Vegas where he once laughed out the door an armed robber. Probably caused the guy to rethink his career path. Uncle Jack urged me in no uncertain terms to take off.

To a youth of deflecting education, then working my way through college at the behest of my folks, I added two years framing Orlando's new flank of apartments with a twenty-three ounce hammer and a B.A. In 1975 I was ready to heed the fun uncle and try freedom of the road. I never heard of Jack Kerouac or the beet generation and I wouldn't have cared if I had. I never liked beets.

The Amazing Kreskin appeared in Orlando. He hypnotized the audience, apparently all but me. He'd say the magic word and I'd watch the Orlando Junior College auditorium erupt into a henhouse. Pretend or otherwise, I realized I wouldn't abdicate control like that, let another entity take me over. The very idea terrified me, kind of like military service.

Never had I surrendered to random chance, run through a shootin' gallery and see where I get hit, drive out and become a wild card in the game of cause and effect; find new spaces to inhabit day to day, populated by people as yet unknown. Always there had been a reason, a time frame, lack of means, a plan or other people to consider. And because of nothing to compare it to, I never thought about it like that.

Now I would drop the reigns and let the horse of happiness have his head, abandon my fate to an indifferent world, just add myself to the mix and experience what was out there. Little did I imagine how seductive it was going to be. I stood on the brink of joining a club for the first time in my life, loose knit though it was. I was about to become what Michener had dubbed a drifter.

I already owned a long, white, oil burning '62 Chevy window van, straight six, three on the tree, chosen for its capacity to carry my jonboat to nearby lakes. It even had a manual choke like a lawn mower; probably the last vehicle before they decided the public couldn't handle that much responsibility, and made chokes automatic. Most days it had no right backfiring out the driveway, much less rolling across country but it had the audacity of nothing to lose and I had some wrenches.

Back then gas stations, also known as service stations, supplied free road maps. Clearly the keys to unlocking the continent, I garnered all I could. Whenever a highway on the map materialized in the actual world, this wondrous correlation was like magic to me. Using one of those maps now, you would expect to drive into the *Twilight Zone* where it's 1975 again. I still have them and I tried it recently, planning to gas up and then fold the map and return to the present. That didn't pan out but they'll get you around without the Interstate.

I introduced to paper maps a gps-reliant friend of my sons. From his fascination I grasped that he was of the wizarding world and I had become a muggle. Open-minded like Arthur Weasley, he found the muggle way marvelous.

Clearer by the day was the fact that I wasn't going to bother amounting to anything. For some reason inaccessible to me, Mom always assumed I'd be a lawyer and she never, *ever* gave that up. But she was not judgmental and a great believer in living life. She put my esquire on hold and made striped curtains and gave me items like a little grill and Tupperware to store food preparations in, fryin' pan, hatchet, Band Aids...; all of which I scorned (I ain't got no need of all that sissy stuff) and every bit of which proved indispensable, topped with the lure that made it all too irresistible - a coffee table book called *Scenic Wonders of America.*

I was optimistic and proud of my muggle-magic carpet. Like a turtle admiring his shell, I gazed into the driver side mirror and saw my van, *my good old boat carrier* holding its own with real vehicles, traveling to destinations unknown through the exotic night air. In the distant future I would see my little boy do the same thing, taking his tractor-trailer truck into the actual gutter in front of the house. I knew what he was feeling as he pushed it along.

I slept on the dead metal floor of it up and down the east coast for a couple years, starting each day tattooed with the rib pattern, wondering where I'd catch my next meal, working very little and savoring it like a saved Christian must welcome rebirth. Not that I wouldn't have appreciated a mattress or at least something soft. Satisfaction with freedom pushed comfort into the realm of overkill. I think I enjoyed all of it. My treacherous memory deletes low points that may have exaggerated the highs, inhibiting me learning from experience.

Never having been in the care of strangers, I had little idea of hospitality. I'd pick up a hitchhiker but I wouldn't take him out of my way and I probably wouldn't offer him any food. I would learn better while traveling, from the generosity of others shown to me.

From the pages of the book surged my first destination - the Outer Banks of North Carolina, photos of wild sand dunes, sounded mighty grand. I bade a hopeful farewell to family and the only home I'd known since a little booger; but Waterloo lay a hundred miles north of Orlando.

My mistake was unearthing an old high school chum in Gainesville, finding him reluctant to answer the door of his apartment for fear of creditors. Probably I had already heard of Bill's roommate's girlfriend. She was very upbeat, I thought, for someone just released from four months in a Mexican jail for smuggling drugs. She said she'd been set-up at the airport with the old "I see you have no carry-on. Would you please take this extra one for me?" trick. Her time had been horrible, "me too" but it was men saying it. She willingly talked about it and she seemed unscarred – maybe just that glad to be out. Finally George McGovern had weighed in.

Having lived at home during college, this was my first stay in a college town. It certainly was fun and conducive to more until I noticed most of my two-hundred smackeroo bankroll had covertly dissolved like cotton candy in the rain. Thus I learned how easily frittered away is money when none is arriving. Shellcrackers and bass from nearby Lake Alice became my source of protein. Dining out toward the end, my friends ate meals while I scavenged jelly packets and crackers from the table.

It's funny how we become connoisseurs of the current staple. I developed scorn for apple butter which seemed a farce and valued the relative substance of strawberry preserves over grape jelly. This, basically, is what I had come to within two hours of my house. I could have turned around, gotten a little work and started again. But that would have been embarrassing. I would learn while traveling that people will endure a lot, even perish ahead of embarrassment. I carried on.

Because it came right eventually, I don't mind admitting this economic crash dulled the initial shine of escape. With money only for gas, I lived on small bass and pickerels I could pull from roadside ditches and swales, frying them immediately over burning sticks in the nearest parking lot, thankful for the little grill Mom had forced on me and the roach-proof Tupperware for keeping bread crumbs in. Yep, those fish probably thought they were safe there. One night I penetrated an aquatic amusement park and caught some sizable bass but tragically most of that bonanza went off from incompetent cooling, ice filched from a motel ice machine apparently not as cold as the kind you buy if you're rich.

This was my first ever grub shortfall, my affronted appetite incited by aromas wafting from roadside eateries. Days of greater abundance had included vegetables I didn't like and wouldn't eat. That luxury no longer held. I finally was ready to eat my black-eyed peas.

My very exciting first ferry floated the van to Ocracoke Island where half the residents are Midgets – some of them quite large. It was a relaxing place to sit on the dock of the bay with an empty stomach but Otis Redding filling my head.

I wasn't the only one craving a solid meal. A school of twenty-inch long weakfish hungrily scoured the open ocean for sustenance, needing plenty to feed everybody. Their lateral line senses began detecting the exact vibrations these toothy predators were hoping for – the water-borne trail of a school of cute li'l pilchards engaged in their own perilous search for plankton. Satisfying hunger makes us vulnerable to the hunger of another.

The terrified feast were feeling the reciprocal pulses of

impending doom as the weakfish pushed them to the surface and toward the neck of Ocracoke Inlet where they would be constricted and easier accessed. But the weakfish were unaware of a new peril just up from Florida.

Expectant seagulls hovering over the distant ripples had caught my eye like a sign over a restaurant proclaiming FREE FOOD. I ran to the van and returned with my ten foot long surf rod. Anxiously I monitored the progress of this telltale surge hoping it would reach at least the outer limit of the rod's amazing casting range. I tied on a heavy, aerodynamic hammered metal Hopkins Spoon and waited. The sea wolves and their commandeered flock reached the inlet and I saw the carnage commence and the birds diving. “Don't cast until you see the whites of their eyes,” George Washington said. “You don't want to spook them with a short cast.” (This is from the benign early period when the Revolutionary War was waged with fishing tackle).

Well, like the British, the fools kept a-comin' and I caught ten and a flounder while saving the lives of at least as many ungrateful pilchards. Instead of eating it, I exercised my atrophied foresight and sold the catch for eleven dollars (65 current gas dollars) to a fisherman who lacked the range. He had failed to badger his son and son's girlfriend into catching more than one lowly catfish and he himself had caught nothing; yet he was quite proud to show that still he could wind up with the fish. His moral victory turned out to be my key financial move.

The Outer Banks was amazing to me but not the biting black flies that owned the beach. You'd spray yourself up for the advance down to the surf and it was okay; but they knew people tasted a lot better coming out and they'd be laying for you. Strange that future-me would return better heeled in a crummier van of a different color and learn to pilot a hang glider there, something I hadn't even heard of yet.

Ensconced behind the wheel at the government campground,

refreshed as a hobo from a cold sulphur water pump shower and pondering what further part of the world to intrude upon, I switched on my good old van radio just in time for a recommendation, a cosmic hint I could not dismiss. It was a lot farther, farther than I'd ever been from Mrs. Boxall, but I'd seen it in my book and I had faith in my radio. Those fish bought me the gas to find out if Peggy Lee would steer me wrong.

4

Wellfleet welcomed me and my seven dollars and offered no hope of employment after Labor Day. Or enjoyment, two normally incompatible ments now oddly inseparable. Often I have come to things late and Cape Cod, it seemed, was another one. My wealth was reserved for emergency bar stool rental on the many rainy nights so I ate baby bluefish until I can still gag at the thought of it (I'm gagging now). Day in and day out I engorged the same easily amassed meal for breakfast, lunch and supper – four baby blues burned plain and dry on my grill and pyre of sticks down at the town wharf where I caught them. After awhile a pep talk was necessary for initiating the task.

"You don't need to enjoy eating anymore," I coached myself. "It's just a way to stay alive." Of course that begged the question of how important that was, less all the time it seemed. My menu varied once when I caught some white perch from the Duckfleet Pond.

At least my diet is very healthy, I thought positively. Then my radio warned me that bluefish that year had unusually high levels of Mercury. Oh well. Thanks, radio. Maybe I'll become the first human thermometer.

I presented myself to a restaurant owner and proposed he buy bluefish from me.

"You mean to say you have a source for bluefish?" he asked incredulously.

"I sure do," I said, popping a couple buttons.

"Where you from son?"

"Florida," I replied proudly, thinking "and I already figured out how to catch bluefish up here."

"Well how do you like that? Danged if it doesn't take a foreigner to come up here and show us what we got."

I absorbed the glory with the modest calm of a man accustomed to it while raising the price in my head.

"You betcha," he said, thumbs in his belt. "I'll take all you can get me. Top dollar too. You wouldn't have any air for sale would you? How about bad news? Man can't have too much of that. Come to think of it, I've been craving daylight lately. Seems I keep runnin' out ev'ry day around sunset. Put me down for a bushel. Man better stock up when he meets a fellow with your kind of connections."

"I think I've got you covered. Anything else?"

"No, that'll do for now."

In this way I learned how common are bluefish to a Cape Codder.

Every night I surf-cast for stripers a couple hours or until my arm fell off. These fish were not so common and more highly esteemed. A good striper would bring about thirty bucks but I never caught one.

Shuffling through the quaint downtown, I eyed greedily the Snickers bars through the window of one store. I hoped a time would come when I could walk right in there and buy one.

"Got any Snickers bars?" I'll say, like I don't know.

"Well, yes."

"Gimme your best one," I'll insist. "I don't care what it costs."

"I'm afraid they're all the same price," the unimaginative clerk will say.

"Well then," I'll respond grandly, "I'll take two."

Just like that.

The author grants that so far a pretty germane question would be, "What's the point?" Another one could be "You drove a thousand miles for this?" And there's always the time honored "So now what?"

Oh ye of little faith - Just when questions like those start looming on the horizon, here comes a beautiful sunrise:

To inter those doubts, the reader must imagine that she (or he) is a woman sunbathing on the narrow spit of beach below the town wharf, relishing every sunbeam that lovingly caresses you, cognizant how fleeting are these fragile emissaries from the cosmos in the face of winter on the way. Fully engaged, you are enchanted by tiny wavelets as they genuflect before you upon the sand. As lying in the sun always turns your thoughts to romance, you conjure the man of your dreams to sweep you away to candlelight dinner.

Enter some guy who drove aimlessly all the way there from Florida to live on bluefish. You don't yet know he exists, nor he you. Will this real live adventure man appear and stride into your daydreams or, having cleaned his four lunch-fish on the wharf above, will he just blindly toss over a big gob of guts?

How many of literature's great love stories begin with, "He never would have known she was there but for the garbled scream." None that I know of. It certainly wasn't "Oh Romeo, Romeo, wherefor art th...blurgumsprogouffblooey. Oh. There thou art Romeo." or "But soft, what guts through yonder window break..."

On the since compiled Yahoo! List of Defective Ways to Introduce Yourself to a Woman, "Throw guts in her mouth and then apologize," ranks near the top and so now I know why that was that. If only I'd had the internet in those days. It turns out, that very offering is key to courtship in a remote corner of Northern France. Just my luck I nail the ritual and she's not from there.

Read the list and you'll see that all the worse ways result in the woman inadvertently dying, which of course eliminates hope for almost everybody. Unfortunately when you're in the top five, there's not much practical difference. But you can see what I mean. The trip's looking up.

Continuing the pattern of Good God Almighty smiling on me when I allow her to, I landed a job murdering lobsters and clams at the Bayside Lobster Hutt for money plus all I could eat. The crusty old pirate who owned the place and his incongruous gay son regretted the little addendum, shocked by what that meant. Actually afraid to be hungry once I had a choice, every night after stuffing myself with burgers, I'd take to the van all the orphan baked potatoes as a hedge against the possibility. Some of the potatoes may have gone off, as I began detecting an unwholesome odor within me.

As a kid at Stake 'n' Shake with my parents, I loved to mix a bite of burger in my mouth with some chocolate shake. I yearned to just pour the shake on the burger like gravy and eat it that way. Finally I had the opportunity to live that fantasy. It was all I imagined it would be and made quite an impression on the old pirate.

Before hunger became a factor, I would have taken no part in boiling live lobsters for restaurant diners. They curl on hitting the water. I assumed this a meaningless reflex but later I was apprised of the obvious, that this is to protect their belly. I was sorry to learn how quickly overcome are my principals and how easily vanquished the quality of mercy. If harder pressed, no telling what I might be capable of. But perhaps morals are for the satisfied. Years later in a Rhode Island restaurant one lobster remained in the tank and my lady friend became emotionally involved with it. The chef was sympathetic to the lonely survivor's plight and cut me a deal on it. What a sucker. I took it home and boiled that baby up. Just kidding. We drove to Naragansett Bay, untaped its claws and turned it loose. They don't feed them in the tanks to discourage defecating and this one stayed right where I'd placed it, picking bits of algae off the rocks and putting them in its mouth. Lobsters can live longer than people, so that one may well be out there now with an appreciation of its freedom keener than most.

And that Snickers bar? It was the best ever. Thanks, Good God Almighty.

In the next paragraph I enter upon an actual enjoyable standard of living, sponsored, as it were, by a certain standard of dying. Not too shabby, didn't take all that long. Sure it includes working but just then working had picked up a little cachet.

The monsoon moved on and the best time ever moved in - recreationally thumbing up and down the Cape, fishing for fun, not survival and swimming in kettle ponds. Thumbing there was world class easy. One beautiful day, so indifferent to getting a ride, I just lay down in some shade with a thumb poking out the grass like a sprinkler head. Being alive under a tree was good enough for me. Not two minutes and a car pulls over. The guy gets out laughing like St. Nick and he says "I don't believe you." And that's the rules, I had to get in his car. It's a lesson in salesmanship – act like you don't care. A man of means, I bought the occasional grocery at Tony and Joe's and I noticed I was always given ninety percent off by the cashier. So I even found love in Old Cape Cod.

I got a pal too, a local artist named Paul Roberts who rented a room off Main Street. He was twenty-nine and had not found love and I felt a little sorry for him to be without at that advanced age. His dream was to walk across Spain with his guitar. Whenever I think of him I wonder if he's done it. I looked forward to a ritual we observed most mornings in front of his toaster. I brought the Arnold cracked wheat and he cooked it. That's what they call a symbiotic relationship. It may seem pitiful but I was gaining a keen view into the delights of small pleasures.

One morning Paul had a surprise waiting for me. He suggested I shut my eyes as he placed on his record player music I never had heard, but has since been among my favorites, the beautiful Concerto d'Aranquez, featuring guitar and orchestra.

Paul was tossing some beach scenes he wasn't satisfied with. I was surprised to find I wouldn't stand this treatment of art and I snatched the canvasses and hung them in the van. That pretty much made it perfect.

Who winters on the Cape automatically gets welfare because there are no jobs. Paul had endured the previous winter. “I sent the check back,” he said. “I knew if I took it, I'd sit around inside all winter. That way I had to get out and get work painting signs.”

I thought that was pretty brave. I'd have at least hung onto the check as a hedge against hard times.

Paul was an interloper in the local art scene and the Wellfleet Art League sent down some thugs one night to work him over. I arrived in the morning with bread bag in hand only to find Paul's toaster overturned, his record collection scratched up and him on the floor with a dune scene split over his head between beach and horizon. Livid with revenge I ...(None of what I just wrote is true. The narrative was getting awfully dull and I had to do something.)

Inevitably the lovely Indian summer went the way of the Indians and Cape Cod turned a cold shoulder to me. My van warmer returned to the mainland, I had no sleeping bag and my white van started resembling a Fridgidaire. I got laid off at the Lobster Hutt and my dollars dwindled. My new goal in life became temporary warmth. To achieve that I would sacrifice a quarter at the public hot shower at the wharf. One night I snuck into the Duck Fleet Inn, closed myself up in one of the common bathrooms and filled the claw-foot tub with hot water to sit by it like Ireland warms itself by the Gulf Stream.

Even most locals don't stick around through winter and my visit was all too clearly coming full circle so I mozied home for Christmas by way of West Springfield, awash with my expanded idea of what was out there. But Peggy Lee had come through like a champ. I did fall in love with Old Cape Cod, just as she said I was sure to do.

5

A lot of people get where they want to be by building a tunnel to there from here. It may not be their optimum tunnel, but they can kick back in it and enjoy the ride. If it's solid, they'll reach their terminus undetoured by threatening side trips; kind of like taking the Interstate where you sacrifice the journey for the destination.

Time was I could have benefited from a tunneling coach. After hitting the road, what's the point? The fact of going was the thing, the beginning of sacrificing the goal for the journey. Places I'd be in five years were not even on the frontier of my imagination and I could not have fathomed what would lead to them. It was an astounding era of constantly moving into an inconceivable future. I have wondered if anything as good would have happened if I were a rich man.

Yet maybe I had slipped into a fool's paradise, immensely satisfied if I wasn't confined in time or space, freedom of movement all that mattered. As a young'un I burned with curiosity of nature and had aspired to explore the ocean. Later I hoped to parlay college into that. I had envisioned the result with no plan to get there and a tunnel built to Bithlo, where I spent an inordinate chunk of time hunting used parts for my junker.

After four years studying the wrong stuff at the wrong school, but enjoying intramural sports, I had nothing to parlay. I recall words from the school guru and philosophy prof who did what he could to help. “You'd be such a marvelous human being,” he said, “if you'd only learn to play the game.” If I'd understood exactly what he meant, I might have profited from those words. But probably not. Games without a ball didn't hold much interest.

Post graduate discontent with swinging a hammer eight to twelve hours a day with nary a word of inspiring conversation, the gift of speech pared-down to "How %&#$!* up" the speaker was the previous night and how many Ludes that required; and a feline holy grail that stands as an entity, apparently connected to nothing, perhaps just a concept and as such unattainable, led me to wander. Of the many roads, marine scientist is my major highway not traveled. Ardent self-appreciation has forestalled envy but I came mighty close with Jacques Cousteau. Imagine the intoxication of being the only man on Earth with scuba gear. And a boat. (To do more than imagine it, read *The Living Sea.)*

Next August the van still was able to burn oil so it burned it all the way to Maine where a successful day was redefined. I had only to coerce myself to dive into the heartstoppingly, skin shatteringly freezing southern extremity of the Arctic Ocean there. I started fighting to get out before I'd even hit the water, hoping to figure out some way to miss it entirely. Naught was required beyond that display of raw courage, I was that pleased with myself, pasting the entire day irrevocably in the plus column. I tried to get 'er done early to devote less time to dreading it and more to having it over with and the exquisite sensation of warming up after.

Of course a hundred feet down-beach from my little diving rock were various Mainiacs standing around and floating in the lethal liquid like it was a Jacuzzi, hoping to diminish my achievement. Which only shows how petty people are and that courage is tailor made, as it should be.

Supper included cliffside sunset and a little Boone's Farm by the park road. A unique bar in Bar Harbor gave me my favorite bar song, *The Port of Amsterdam,* by any standard not a family friendly composition. He sang that in the first set. Each set defeated its predecessor for raunchiness and those who stuck with him to 2 a.m. heard the man sing of bestiality.

I fell back to Cape Cod and popped into the Lobster Hutt. They weren't hiring but the old pirate thought I looked familiar. Then with a sense of wonder he said, “Aiy! You're the crazy guy poured a frappe all over his burger.” Still distinguishing myself.

I got hired to wash dishes at the prestigious Wellfleet Oyster House. This fine old establishment in a Victorian Cape house was the poster child for “You can't judge a book by its cover.”

If the customers could have seen from their fancy, doilied tables into the kitchen after eating their high-dollar pre-digested cuisine, they'd have needed psychiatric care. And they'd never eat in a restaurant again. My most enduring image is the platters of food awaiting someone to bring them out. Unless he went by shape, there was absolutely no way a waiter could tell what meal was on what platter until he picked it up. Then the solid blanket of blue-bottle flies lifted off and like magic the corruption appeared. In other, less natural venues this effect is achieved by lifting off a cover dome. If only the flies would have stuck long enough for the customer to witness the wonder of it.

As instructed, I scraped off the plates and back into the jar all incompletely used condiments. The fish usually stank on exiting the fridge because nothing could be past its prime. And the cook cared naught for staggered cooking times. If a decomposing flounder fillet and a prime rib occupied the same order, they went in together and remained side by side until the beef was done. Maybe that was to burn out the stink of the rotting fish. A little Portuguese guy named Tony ran that fly circus.

Egalitarian that he was, Tony got his chefs by a dishwasher ascending to the post. He was frustrated and angry at my lack of ambition. I guess I was a blockage in the line.

“You're a smart guy, Tom,” he flattered me. “Why you don't want to move up?”

“Tony,” I said, “you need a new chef, hire another dishwasher and just make him the chef. He'll figure it out.”

I got a better offer anyway. A young woman discovered me surf fishing with my giant rod and started filming like she'd spotted Bigfoot. Not far off, she considered me some rare and strangely natural modern barbarian. It was the casting that really seemed to get her. She couldn't get enough footage of that. A well heeled film student and gourmet chef, she offered me free lodging and hearty meals on Manhattan, that I might pursue writing. Bingo! It was like Tarzan going home with Jane but, like any natural man, I was easily lured from the grisly alternative of gainful employment. I drove my trusty home out to her cousin's house on Long Island, naturally, parked it on the street and rode the train jon (4th class) to captivity.

She had been all over the world, it seemed, as had every single one of her friends. I hadn't known anybody who'd even been to Europe and, provincial and chronically low on funds, I never entertained the thought of it. This lent me an unfamiliar sense of inferiority. It was the doorman who found my presence the most puzzling. Every time I entered his domain, it renewed his surprise at seeing me the first time. I had one pair of sneakers and a pair of jeans and he assessed their decline over my six month stay. My sneakers were too tight so I swapped with a guy living on the sidewalk whose pair were too loose and we both achieved perfection. During that transaction I was accused by a passerby of stealing his shoes. When the blizzard of '77 shut down the city with the first snow I had seen since a child, my wardrobe's lack of depth had the unforeseen consequence of limiting my time playing in it.

It also prevented me meeting Lauren Bacall at the *Applause* cast party across the street. In the home stretch my duds faltered. I went back and watched it on tv. Who needs them anyway? I was a star in my own right as an extra in pretty much every NYU student film.

My term in New York received great meaning not from new people but survivors from the past. No one had been back since our flight in 1958 but there still were people who remembered my parents. My father's sister, in her eighties, learned I was in town and beckoned me.

I had seen my Aunt Rae only once in my adult life, when she and Uncle Nat briefly called on my father after his cancer diagnosis. We visited at her Greenwich Village apartment, a short walk from my digs on Fifth Avenue. With rent control she had this prime location for very little. I had heard only bad things about her but she was captivating to talk with. I was considering amending my impression when she sensed a sympathetic ear and tried to turn me against Arnie whom she said had betrayed her. She was put out when I failed to take her side. In her old age with gender gone I could see the face of my father, something I did not expect ever to see without being able to talk to him. It was disconcerting, like seeing a ghost, but in a way, I thought, closer than I expected to come to it again, some of the same genes here.

My aunt informed the Bernsteins of my presence; not the Leonard Bernsteins but the family of my father's best friend from childhood. Parting geographically as we did, I never knew he had such a friend and had left him behind. It happened that right then Robbie was lingering at the exit, apparently loathe to float through. They sent for me.

I knew none of these people and it put me in mind of what a latecomer I was to my father's life, seventy percent of it before I made the scene. Robbie's daughter Naomi was there and she seemed to have a crush on Arnie, rhapsodizing "what a beautiful man he is, with eyelashes any woman would kill for." I never thought eyelashes were so important. I spoke to Robbie at his bedside and I still remember his kind face and gentle demeanor. It was quite moving that this was the face of my father's friend through life in America. The times they must have had!

As Dad visited me in Aunt Rae, he visited his old pal in me. Then Robbie floated on through. His family said that seeing the son of David Levine brought him full circle and he was able to let go. As we will seek something good at such times, they felt very good about me showing up and they believed it was no accident.

So did I randomly drive up the coast for want of anything better to do or, as Naomi felt, had I been directed by unseen forces from Florida to her father's bedside? Maybe my van really was a magic carpet.

On a roll, I decided to investigate if Maude Blackman, our beloved housekeeper from the old days, still existed. I remembered her like a second mother, or maybe a grandmother. Maude had been quite a person. Mom used to say you can tell your real friends because they don't call and ask if you need help, they show up. When hard times got harder, Maude showed up. Quite the class act, Maude prepared Anne Morrow for her wedding to Charles Lindbergh.

There had been two decades since my mother sought refuge in Florida: Viet Nam, Alaska statehood, Cuban Sandwich Crisis, Martin King, the Civil Rights Act, man on the moon, my dad gone, my big sister married, my little sister grown up, Mom head nurse at Holiday Hospital - a lot of water over the damn dam and me shootin' out the spillway yahooin' on a leaky innertube. Even if I did find Maude, she probably wouldn't remember who I was and it wouldn't mean much to her if she did. But scrunched among the millions in the foot thick phone book, there was her husband's name by an address and a disconnected number so I bused across town, then walked. As I got close a tall chain link fence barricaded my way. With no visible way around it I had to climb into the neighborhood. Pointy-toed shoes would have been very helpful. I wondered if the fence was to keep people out or keep people in.

I did not know there could be, in the United States, such barren civilization as this, like a wasteland. I found the address in an apartment building besieged by dirt - a cruddy, fetid dirt that brooked no origin in nature, unable even to invite weeds. Access was through stairs up the middle of a series of landings. On the tenant buzzer list was Lloyd Blackman. Just to make this correlation with the phone book seemed extraordinary. The suspense was building but still the result I hoped for was the least likely of the candidates. I pressed the buzzer.

I was sporting a lot of unkempt curly black hair and a beard. A lean ebony woman appeared three flights up and viewed with suspicion this uncouth looking white-man. “What do you want?” she accused, leaning over the wall.

“I'm looking for Maude Blackman,” I replied.

“There's nobody here by that name.”

That was disappointing to hear but something about this person seemed familiar and I wondered if, wonder of wonders, alive where life was not welcome, this was Maude. I baited the hook. “She used to work for my family a long time ago.”

“Where?” the inquisitor barked skeptically.

“Great Neck.”

“What's your name?” she yelled down.

“Thom...”

She started jumping up and down like she'd been electrocuted and yelled, “Thomas, you get up here right now.”

Sometimes the passage of time has no power at all. This is the moment that made the whole trip north not only worthwhile but necessary. This person had endured in my mind all that time like part of a legend and perhaps I like that in hers. Never had I expected to find her in the physical world.

As commanded, I ran up the stairs to a long overdue hug. Inside, I'd never imagined a door so barricaded as hers, chains and deadbolts the length of it, right down to an angled iron rod from the floor into a notch part way up. It cost her some trouble just to come out and see who was down there. She was living alone, using her husband's name for safety. She was charming and articulate and our visit was a revelation for me. In her eighties Maude's enthusiasm and curiosity about life surpassed that of any young person I knew. We sipped wine and talked as comfortably as old friends. I returned one time more.

This got Maude and Mom back in touch and they discussed getting her down to Orlando but that didn't happen. Maude also contacted my sponsor and kept up with me that way. The whole thing was kind of a tenacious miracle sitting there primed and ready to spring. And it would have been left there, waiting, until it evaporated, never to be realized or known about if I hadn't met a film student on a Cape Cod beach.

It seems pure chance dictates the best of life, delivering where intentions never do, never could, for intentions are a laser and chance diffused. Chance works from the chest far richer in treasure, encompassing all possibilities known and unknown. Without a map I found some of this treasure simply by cutting loose and going with the flow.

Thus I arrived in Manhattan with only fun in mind and started picking up fragments of my exiled family's life and mine twenty years after the shattering. Yes, far more meaningful would have been my parents making this pilgrimage and making it earlier but something had blocked them, leaving it to an ambassador. Kind of surreal how the past can neglected endure and mutate to suit the present. Long after it has been consumed in the fires of moving on, it is hunkered down in isolated locations, waiting to ambush if we pass near enough, soon enough.

Having escaped school and church, my life aspiration had boiled down to escape from work. A day without work was logged a successful one and I'd put together quite a string. Reaching that plateau taught me that indolence is not enough. My closest brush with a writing breakthrough was an editor at the Village Voice I briefly dated. She was excited about my piece on a squirrel rebellion in Lincoln Square and planned to use it, nixed by a higher- up who didn't appreciate a Floridian parody of New York. I needed something more and writing wasn't it. After six months even indolence, it seemed, had its price. What I needed was gas money. I got a job hustling foliage with a couple terrific guys my age never been off the island, Charlie Gofhaulic and Bobby Jones. The mind boggles at what they'd never seen or felt. Only when I invited them over for dinner and they were nervous and giddy coming in the door of the apartment did I understand there were social strata and they were feeling out of theirs. No telling what the doorman was thinking.

That job had a flawed premise. I later found out the boss had an unauthorized relationship with an employee and his wife had hired me to work in the store and show him a thing or two; but he moved me immediately onto the street where the real money was.

People starving for nature couldn't resist buying some; two semi loads of plants a week up from the nurseries in my old home town Apopka. There is unity in the world. Just hard to see the point of it.

Probably it was nightmarish for the plants, greenhouses rife with rumor. “We heard those trucks are all going to New York City.”

“Oh no! Poor Aunt Rhoda.”

“I fear we shall never see her again.”

“Whither thou goest,” opined some sage.

“Why can't they just leaf us alone?” cried a weeping willow.

“Maybe they got a cutting.”

“Yes, maybe. But I doubt it. We're all the same to them.”

“Even if they did,” says an eggplant, “do you really believe that reincarnation fertilizer?”

“I do,” piped up a carnation.

Perhaps they tried intentional wilting to be deemed unsuitable for export. Who knows what went on. Maybe nothing. Maybe plants don't really have any idea what's happening.

But I can truthfully say I have worked on Wall Street. The owner, Jerry, was some brand of quintessential New Yorker, pure elixir of obnoxious. And this could be one potent drink. He'd be out there on a cold windy day, snot dangling from the tip of his nose haranguing some poor pedestrian into buying a plant. Or he could do more.

Most days Charlie, Bobby and I roamed the city with a van full of foliage plants, setting up on a corner and hoping to draw a crowd before we drew cops. If you had people, the cops left you alone like it was a force field. Once, we got arrested but none of us had i.d. for just that eventuality, nobody admitting to driving the van or willing to incriminate himself by doing it now. In anonymity can be security. I remember one officer getting steamed because I felt comfy enough to put my feet up on the table during the interview. They wound up letting us go and towing the van. That wound up Jerry pretty good.

As much as police were a thorn in our foot, having never thought to bribe them, there still was no solidarity among plant sellers. I was surprised that on seeing someone else selling plants, Jerry instantly called the cops, nipping it in the bud. I wouldn't have thought he'd do that; but he played for keeps.

I was natural with this modus operandi and thought I was good at it. But something outlandish Jerry did one day, I've often thought was a revealing lesson in human nature that I was lucky to see but unable to capitalize on:

We have just parked two vans in front of an office building. No contact has been made within and our worlds have not yet collided. Jerry tells us to carry stuff in there – six foot ficus trees, palms, whatever, just keep 'em coming, a bucket brigade of trees. I know nobody has agreed to even look at a leaf. We're waltzing in with these big potted plants, twenty-five to a hundred 1977 dollars each, then putting them down and going for more like it's our private nursery. The guy in his white shirt and tie looks puzzled, asks us what we're doing, we just keep doing it, I can't imagine why and I don't feel good about behaving this way. I figure we'll have to carry them back out again, maybe get in a fight or something. We never saw those plants again. When we had transferred everything from the vans to this office suite, Jerry goes in there to collect his loot.

I witnessed the opening argument and returned to the street. What I would love to know now but didn't care much about then, is exactly how the conversation went. Did Jerry pretend like they'd ordered them? Or did he just say, "Look, #%$&*@!, they're your plants now. Pay up. I got mouths to feed." And if necessary the good old, "I ain't got all day." It could be belligerence is a language there. Or maybe the office denizens trancelike crowded among this instant Eden where all had been metal and vinyl, where nature had at long last found them and intruded upon their mechanization, touching the leaves, loving the branches, feeling stirring in their genes, suggesting rebellion should the oxygen givers be exorcised. Plants – they too would prefer to be outside in the day as it begins cool, then warms in the sun and cools again. But they have come in to yearn with these humans in their isolation and remind them of something. And maybe Jerry, not as green as his product, knew this would happen. He counted on the difference between not furnishing the foliage in the first place and ordering it taken it away.

Any way you prune it, it was shrubbery where the shrubber gives you something of his choosing for your money; the plant sales version of rape. He skips the accord phase, just, "This is what we're doin' now."

You could say he was an urban hero, Rude Robin Hood bringing Sherwood Forest to the peasants.

I have tried from time to time to find a way to broaden the scope of the principles at play there and benefit from them but so far I got nothin'.

My last day I sold an areca palm to a nice old lady for $25.00 (would have been 20.00 in the shop. Everything's dearer on the street because people expect the opposite) and I'm telling her how palms need a lot of sun. Jerry walks right over while I'm talking and tells me to shut up and get back to work and turns to her and says, "Don't worry. They don't need any sun. Put it in the closet. It'll be fine."

The last words I recall from Jerry were, "No
me and expects to keep his job." Oh well. At 25
freelance sales, it was the highest paying job I ever had.

Even in Manhattan April was lovely and I enjoyed stro
over to Washington Square Park where, on the premise that the
were crazy, regularly spaced men vied for subsidies from passersby. Once I heard one accusing the other of being feau crazy, whose entire shtick was loudly playing the boombox on his shoulder next to the genuine articles and spoiling business. The current victim was belittling this lunatic affectation, contrived nuttiness and overall incompetence and blighting of true insanity with his not cool behavior. "You're not crazy," he kept insisting. "I'm crazy." We all hang our hat on something.

The other fellow stood his ground, literally.

Confucious say,

The squirrel of time buries the nuts of tomorrow and eats them yesterday.

I retained a tragic autumn image from that park. I regularly saw what I assumed was the same squirrel industriously burying acorns in a garbage can. Maybe the park was so crowded that actual real estate was acorned out. Boy was he/she in for a hard lesson; might be forced into pillaging the caches of others and becoming a pariah. Or a capitalist.

It surely was a fantastic metaphor for something or someone, never could put my finger right on it.

6

Are you wondering how the grand van has been faring all this time? Thinking maybe all that metal and rubber and glass forgot that it had been molded into a torpedo of freedom from responsibility? That by now it was just dimensions with windows – weight, length, elements? No longer a cohesive team effort to burn fossil fuel and drag my butt around the countryside?

I think I know what you're really asking: Is the Ice Age over? Did the van still live? That's it, isn't it? And was I still worthy of it? Could I still be vandalized? Would the road again be mine? I figured that out because I was asking the same things.

I watched another ambiguous dawn manifest over the East River and thought how pretty that looked. Luckily I had perspective enough left to realize that wasn't a promising sign. That was Charlie and Bobby's idea of a sunrise but I remembered there were better ones to start a day with. I bought my hostess a forty dollar bonsai plant good-bye and on my 27th birthday left as I had come, riding the train jon away from the lap of luxury. I hopped a bus and then walked into the neighborhood until I barely made out a familiar white form, like The Lone Ranger spotting Silver. There it stood against the curb where I left it many surprises ago, eliminated from my world, hopefully no hard feelings.

Wintry weather had returned. Held fast by frozen slush, the tires still had air, frozen air that it might have been. The door's hinges groaned with carthritis as I pried it open and regained the foam rubber and springs behind the wheel, a little disappointed to find the seat no better than I left it, unhealed by disuse. Anyway that's what I have towels for. I gazed around at the good old azure metal interior and reacquainted myself with all the subsistence crap I hadn't seen for so long: my framing hammer, just in case; my faithful Coleman ice chest, that lacks only and ever ice, my genuine sombrero purchased for four bucks at Palmer Feed Store in Orlando. Always, I feel, I must have a sombrero. And of course fishing tackle. Behind my seat is the egg crate of leapfrogging extra parts like the carburetor I have replaced but keep for the day when it's better than the one I replaced it with, which then will assume its position in the crate. Inadequate before, their time will come again. Everything's relative, man, and this is the calculus of my van, constantly spiraling halfway to zero, nearer with each descent. I have learned that palmetto bugs prefer daytime, of all the crannies and nooks of my home, in the spare distributor cap. Thus I find the little Draculas and shake them outside. I believe I have expanded their range. Once tropical they live now in New England. Still only floor to sleep on but after half a year on a waterbed I could handle the stability.

The key had faithfully remained in the ignition switch where I stationed it, not running off with some other more attractive ignition; a good start looking for another one. I hoped the ignition had not grown tired of this key and no longer capable of being turned on by it. Soon we would know.

Two fingers behind the knob pulled out the trusty choke all the way - the gas was old, the engine cold. I optimistically pumped the throttle a few times, the pedal sticking down as it did before, dual feet required to work it, the left lifting from underneath. Then my left foot depressed the creaking clutch. Still my gravest doubts remained to be addressed. They concerned the long slumbering Battery, receiving zero demands for motivation in six months – flabby, used to doing nothing, ruling calmy at the still headwaters of the decommissioned van, upstream of everything, wondering why it was ever born. Was Battery still capable of inspiring ignition? Could it still go with the flow?

The reader might be wondering a new question: Does battery worship exist as a cargo cult?

In case the prime mover has retained juice enough for just one start, knowing with alternator on the team that is enough, I don't want to squander it with an empty carburetor. Heck, I saw *The Flight of the Phoenix.* Sometimes you only get one shot. I pumped the pedal a few times more. It returned of its own accord, as in a dream. Taking this as a sign that all systems were go, I threw her into neutral and let the clutch back out. The key's head nestled at long last between thumb and index finger. Was that a sigh I heard? Love I felt? Did I take a deep breath before finding out everything? Will I just get on with the story? Okay. Drumroll -

With the electric kiss of rotation, Battery remembered why I was sitting there and, consequently, its purpose. The starter, hopeless of receiving another signal had redefined itself as a non-starter. It grunted unwelcome surprise, then barely turned over the engine a few agonizing times. When the spark plugs caught on and my rusty steed roared from hibernation to liberation, cogitation to carburation, inspiration to palpitation, frustration to a wide-open nation... I was a little surprised and real happy. Such a portentous roar that was, the one truly exciting, blood boiling sound of technology. "Fire all of your guns at once and explode into space." Don't mind if I do. After a few rev-ups, choke back in halfway, we lurched from the slush. Yahoo! Free again, only this time free from three squares and no job, everything I wanted. Whoda thunk it? Could it be dissatisfaction must follow satisfaction? I wonder if anybody ever noticed the van was gone.

Anyway, what a battery! I don't know how I happened to have such a good one but it has been my standard ever since for what a battery ought to be.

So what do you do with your dream-come-true in the rear view mirror? Maybe fade it to the vanishing point. As a kept man

I was heavier than I'd ever been, 190 pounds with my first little spare tire 'round my waist, something to live off in the leaner times ahead. Heater inoperative and wind biting me from the rusted-out floor *and* whistling through the bullet hole above the windshield and the incompletely rolled up windows, I aimed my magic carpet south to get warm, then hung a right at Virginia.

I stopped in on Pat, Arnie and their daughter Kim in Germantown, of all places, Tennessee (where my brother was quite the curiosity, generally alluded to as "that smart talkin' feller) and of all people, who answers the door but li'l sis', just happens to be visiting. They never believed we hadn't arranged it. So I had a great semi-family reunion; and witnessed the spectacle of my brother in his own yard, shirt off pulling weeds, cigaret drooping out the corner of his mouth. I got a job for a few weeks with an obnoxious guy building houses one at a time and financed womanfest destiny.

West unfolded glacially in front of a long, blue cloud marking my progress on the abandoned Route 66, the van's top speed down to 45 mph. I was rolling so slow cowboys waved at me from horseback. Probably they'd seen the billowing anaconda for some time and wondered what it was chasing. My most compelling mental debate was the choice between free gas forever and free food. I settled on free food because if the van stopped going, at least I could eat. A secondary debate was beautiful naked girl by the road holding a pizza. That one was easier. I quickly chose the pizza. So I was ready with my answers should the offers come. Stomach seemed to be calling the shots. Of course if they came in that order and the free food already secured, the second one might come down to toppings.

Easing into endless space like that, left leg out the window, cruise control brick on the gas pedal and steering with the other knee so I could play the trumpet or harmonica or make a pb&j on Saltines made me feel like all my time had been in a sardine can.

My guidebook, *Scenic Wonders of America* had shown me Big

Sur, California. It sounded and looked amazing and that was the farthest extent of my hopes. Cosmically enough, as I crossed the California line my more-than-just-a-radio started playing the Route 66 tv show theme music. That's right, Buzz, Todd and me. I had fun for a while in Ocean Beach with my new buddy Grant who was living on an empty sailboat. We had "all sports days" and went to Mexico twice, once on his Honda 350 and once in the van. What a blast. Then I weighed anchor for Big Sur.

Barely able to struggle up a hill anymore, bicyclists passing me, at El Refugio State Beach the heroic engine could serve me no longer and went out with a bang, 250 miles shy. Without other prospects, I did not relish my return to subsistence fishing. A few weeks later an event would prove something I had suspected - that this van was equipped with an infinite improbability drive. Impossible to do on purpose, this is my most compelling argument for the primacy of random chance over intentions.

I was a little lonely, thinking I didn't know anybody for thousands of miles and my van is caput, but a guy in a fifties powder-blue Chevy pick-up pulled over and offered to tow the dead body to Goleta and hire me to paint houses. On board with this upward trend, a local dumpster there gave me sandwiches (unfortunately from a health food store and therefore inedible) and a king-size mattress. If you haven't carried one of these by yourself a couple blocks and then tried to squeeze it into a van or a toothpaste tube, you can't entirely grasp the word "unwieldy." A cop made me push my deluxe bedroom off the street and into an apartment parking lot. A couple weeks and some painted houses later, I was looking at a motorcycle I might trade the van for and someone behind me called my name.

I turned to see a grandson of Aunt Violet, my Missouri cousin whom I hadn't seen or thought much about in ten years and had no idea what part of the planet he was on. My van's twenty-year odyssey from the Detroit assembly line had finished in the parking space exactly behind Harry's apartment. Was that long range engineering or just style? Turned out he was a student at USC. Out of millions of Californians, my magic carpet, needing no engine contrived to find the only one I was related to. How Harry recognized me from behind and so out of context remains a lovely mystery. Then I stayed awhile longer and we had fun and got to know each other. I had almost left with neither of us ever knowing. What a waste of serendipity *that* would have been. Imagine I had been tasked when leaving New York with finding my cousin without a clue while making sure my van engine blows within towing range of him. I'd never have even tried.

Surely you're thinking, "Enough with the family reunion. I want to know if a measly rod thrown through the engine wall could stop the almighty force of freedom."

Let me just say, "Not with the infinite improbability drive still intact."

What to my wondering eyes did appear, not a team of reindeer but an engine by the road for fifty bucks. Had it fallen out the sky? Ridden a glacier there like an erratic boulder? Been upchucked by an engineer? Was it just any engine, a Ford or Chrysler, a Chevy V-8? Or was it the same exact Chevy straight six as in the van?

Might as well have had my name on it. Probably did somewhere. To heck with the motorcycle! I got it for thirty and got it in for a hundred with a guy lost a few fingers to a radial arm saw and needed the work. Got to be one crummy moment – fingers one second, stumps the next. Made it to Big Sur and then some.

A magical year more of freedom from success (which included lots of things like four hand poker for matchsticks in the revitalized van in an Arizona mountain ghost town blizzard, and enjoying a four hand massage in Oak Creek Canyon under the full moon and coyotes serenading in the distance, impressive to a Florida boy) and then I lucked into lucrative work that included neither boss nor confinement nor writing.

From a chance encounter with a young woman selling baskets

from a bicycle I became a peddler of a multitude of household products under forty bucks from an Atlanta company called Wholesale Merchandise, a business model I would stick with for twenty years. I showed a knack for it because it's like fishing, my first week number one in the country. It didn't come with an esquire but Mom was pretty pleased, said it couldn't happen to a better person. For the first time ever, at 29, I had extra money. I bought myself a destination called Europe.

7

Mid summer 1979 I left the only continent I'd ever seen with the sole idea of standing thumb-out by a tree-lined country road on a continent composed entirely of hearsay and maybe a hay wagon full of girls picks me up. *Two for the Road* must have planted that notion. Probably it was not thirst for adventure and the unknown but that movie and feeling provincial around film students that made me go.

The West and my introduction to the existence of backpacks had lured me into hiking and camping which I never had considered doing and showed how liberating is tent to foot traveler - wander where you want and know you will have lodging, like a van but off-road. It frees the mind as well as the feet. Mom had got me a backpack for Christmas. I brought it and a small tent to Europe and this became my habit.

My plane landed in Luxembourg which I supposed was the capital of Germany or something. With only a vague notion of Europe's location, I certainly had no idea where individual parts like Germany might be. Three days walking around Luxembourg City got me to a store where I could buy a road map of Europe and find myself. But there wasn't a name on it I recognized. To my credit I deduced that if the map were in English, there would have to be *something* familiar. I did go to school. So I concluded the map must be written in European.

I really thought that, though now that I'm more worldly it seems strange. We all have our little gaps. But with the advent of the Eu, who knows? I may have been forward thinking.

With time I was able to decode it a little, things like Venezia probably was Venice and Roma almost certainly was Rome. I finally figured out Firenzia must be France, which I had not realized was in Italy (*Italia*).

I contend that this level of awareness is more common among Americans than the reader would like to think. Hell. The reader's probably there. It's just that most of us don't export it. Either we bone up or we don't go. I didn't have time to bone up.

I found out the map was written in German, which seemed a mean joke. Maybe maps were their consolation prize. But who needs maps anyway? I might as well just head south. Outside Luxembourg City I found myself thumb-out by that envisioned country road, enjoying the dappled shade of Europe. Mission accomplished. But the timing was off. Here comes fifty-something Argentine engineer Hugo Vasquez on a lonely vacation. He was a great introduction and looking back, I wouldn't trade Hugo for any hay wagon.

I will share here a little of Hugo, from whom I learned much in two days. The banal stood no chance against him. He would exalt it.

Never would Hugo merely stop to eat, for that would squander a God-given opportunity for a picnic. Each meal was fueled by a shopping spree culminating in the hunt for a worthy setting. Our digestion found some spectacular venues. Before the border he hunted up a self-serve car wash so his white chariot would enter Switzerland proud and clean.

Hugo had terminal EHS, or extreme hospitality syndrome. This and machismo made an ordeal of our late arrival in Switzerland but one I would not wish to have missed. All hotels were booked solid so through the Swiss night he drove like a mythical hero in search of lodging. Miserably craving sleep I implored him to stop the car and let me lie down by the road. “You can pick me up in the morning,” I assured him.

But I was in his care and the thought horrified him. “No, I

cannot," he answered.

To my overwhelming joy, the next place we tried had a room but when the clerk told him it had only one bed, Hugo's skin visibly crawled with disgust and he refused it.

"Just get the room," I pleaded. "I'll sleep on the floor. If you don't, I'll walk out the door and sleep on the lawn."

A lesser man would have let me flatten the grass. With the gravity of a priest recanting his vows, Hugo agreed to the room but not with the result I expected. Fully clothed he got on the bed and I lay down blissfully on the floor at its foot and said, "Good night." After a period of silence Hugo sat up and extended his hand down to me, I supposed to shake it. I clasped his hand and with surprising strength he pulled me over the footboard and onto his bed.

"You cannot have less than I have," he said. Then he wagged his finger at me. "But we must never speak of this."

Well, I not only spoke of it but now it's in a book. If you're reading this, Hugo, let me say in my defense, I never actually agreed to that.

I felt like pinching myself that I was in Switzerland because it was such a famous place. The reader should not be stunned to learn, though, that I was surprised by the Alps because I had thought them in the Himalayas. Which I had sense enough to be pretty sure weren't in Europe.

Hugo offered to take me anywhere in Europe I wanted to go but there was no such place. I felt it was time to give the hay wagon a second chance. We parted sadly in Zug, where I learned that Swiss cheese there is just called cheese. I fished a little in Lake Zug with no success.

This time some Belgians interceded on the hay wagon, driving me down that well worn path from the sublime to the ridiculous while demonstrating why people of this nation are considered special. In our brief association the woman in the back seat bounced around and squealed if she saw a train and the driver took us on a thrill ride up a highway exit ramp where I watched terror grow on the face of the frantically braking Mercedes driver whose grill stopped inches from meeting ours. (I had heard with skepticism that a Belgian driver license could be purchased at Woolworth's for twenty-five cents. Suddenly I was sure it was true.)

They got low on gas on a day when the gas stations were closed. "Ciuso!" the "driver" spat every time on seeing the sign, each successive exclamation with heightened anguish until mercifully, they ran out in Como, probably saving my life and untold others. I exercised the delightful hitchhiker's prerogative of simply grabbing my pack and strolling away from the problem.

Lucky for me they hit empty in the vicinity of Heather and Dennis Patterson of Newtownyards, North Ireland, camping with their friends, 18 -year old Allison and her boyfriend who worked at Belfast Woolworth's and informed me that a pair of Levis there cost a hundred dollars. They brought me to the campground where flowed their river of Scotch. The night was cold and damp and the fiery fluid the sole source of warmth in my gullet. With no space for my tent, I lay outside theirs in my sleeping bag sneezing. Compassionate Heather prevailed over a reluctant Dennis who had other ideas and they invited me inside and cozy. This Europe place was turning out great!

I developed the new sport of horrifying Europeans with my ignorance of their rinkydink continent; especially the insecure Dutch, with their man-made geography and finger-in-the-dike heroes. They feared I represented all Americans. If I were feeling particularly playful, I would allude to my college degree.

Reflecting on it, I suppose I am a typical American. My initial stage featured three interests: fishing, playing ball and fishing. In the next phase my mind expanded to include millions of new interests, all under one heading. Furthermore in school they make Europe very distasteful for boys. They stand up art and literature around it like a fortress to repel any possible curiosity of the place.

They don't intrigue us as they could with important items such as certain beaches in Greece that, lacking palm trees are lined instead with naked Scandinavian girls and no lack of coconuts; or the amazingly cheap wine to be had in Italy. Who knows? Maybe they don't want us to go.

By Greece's Corfu Island I was running out of land, rides and daylight, so got on a bus. At the end of the line I shouldered my pack and set sneaker to ground, still unsure where it was on a map. Stumbling downhill in the dark over fences and through pig farms and everything else in the line of unseen obstacles and traps, I hoped I was descending toward the sea. Being lost was emerging as a better bet when I started hearing horrible music. Aiming for the sound, I fell out the bushes at a tent disco on the beach. I stashed my backpack in a shrub and investigated this marvel, bye the bye introducing myself to Ouzo.

Sometimes it's great when locations don't intersect with time, like my pack coinciding with the young man staggering over and Europeein' on the shrub. Most surely by the grace of Good God Almighty, I retrieved it just before that happened.

Upon awakening in the morning, I became astounded by blonde women all across the hillside stepping unadorned from their tents and stretching like fairies emerging from their flowers. Like I said, who needs a map you can read? It could only cause you trouble. I had blindly stumbled into the Pubonic Teutonic Plague, a fleshorama without the drama, the European renowned Pelekas Beach, no pelicans but pelekass aplenty, mecca for northern Europeans to walk around like babies in front of themselves.

Sadly the nudity created a sensory overload and young women walking around naked became unremarkable; no doubt a survival trait from eons past that let me concentrate on more important things. I purchased a mask and snorkel, something I never again would travel without and it was two weeks of almost constant fun, rising with the sun, developing my trick frisbee catches with a local octopuserman, snorkeling, once chasing a clever squid that tried to lose me in a cute little ink cloud. I suppose because I never ate him, he thought that totally disoriented me.

There had been a time when I mourned the passing of the age of exploration. That was premature. For me this ranks with anything Lewis and Clark might have strolled into and I'm pretty sure they would agree. My small step for a man was exiting the bus. The hard part was knowing it had been going on for so long without me.

One day I sat beside a long-haired Afrikaner atop a domed, towering rock we had climbed up the back side of, trying to corral the nerve to leap from it into the Ionian Sea, far, far below; almost out of sight. As it is with such things, the longer we waited, the more we wanted to do it just to have it over with but the less likely it felt that we would, the more desperate the suspense, the more fun time squandered and the greater potential for shame. And why were we putting ourselves through this in the first place? Who knows. That's evolution for you – it includes behaviors whose survival value is no longer clear.

My fellow sufferer must have glimpsed himself an old man wishing he'd leaped or worse, still sitting there trying to. Suddenly he sprang up screaming and ran across the rock into the air. In order to assign full value to his brave test jump, I walked to the edge and assured myself of his survival before following.

I never went naked because really, why would you, though my constant bathing suit was wearing to rags. We don't realize how our little perversities may adversely effect the lives of others. I finally removed my tatters to go swimming, probably to extend their life. This was an event two non-naked lady tourists had been waiting for, shamelessly photographing me as I strode back out. Said one of them, “It's about time.”

I had been selfishly holding them up. They must have gotten everyone else and needed the Prince of Pelekas to seal their collection.

A comic sight was these bony, unclad guys strutting up and

down clutching a cool toilet paper roll, as they all had been visited by surprise shitting. I didn't really get it. Already naked, they could just step into the water. Maybe it was a macho thing. My own solid, predictable product allowed me to look upon them smugly until the fateful day I drank some random water and made oatmeal with the sea; which led to one of my fondest memories of Greece.

I had agreed to wait tables that evening for a free moussaka at a taverna up the hill. The serving method was to take all the orders, they cook all the meals together and I bring them to the patio all at once in a devastating tsunami of olive oil and pasta. But due to my new condition I never made it all the way out with the trays, setting them down and dashing to the outhouse for more pressing business.

Luckily this was the one outhouse on the beach furnished with that priceless panacea of the afflicted, toilet paper – a striking act of compassion from the proprietor or he suspected it would draw business. So frequent were my visits that when I entered and found no roll, I knew exactly who was the dirty dog. It had to be the Dutch guy who just exited because I also had immediately preceded him. Either he had come up short for his own needs or he hoped to dole it out on the beach for personal favors or cash. Worse, this guy, as Dutch guys will, regularly pontificated on his own high moral standards. I think toilet paper thieves get this way by comparing themselves to their German neighbors. Everything's relative.

The Lying Dutchman thunk he had pulled off the perfect crime. But he didn't count on Detective Dan Diarrhea traveling all the way from Florida to thwart his assturdly plan of wiping with impunity. On being confronted, he denied the charge but I knew I was right and persisted until he produced the purloined paper. Foiled in his attempt on the only stationary roll on the beach, he must have resorted to ambush, casually walking by one of the mobile rolls, snatching and running. The victim's shouts would have rallied the others who took hot pursuit, streaming across Pelekas. It's not a pretty scene, but it's a European one.

The customers grew impatient of my condition so the anxious proprietor handed me a bottle of red wine, instructing with hand signals that I chug it. Luckily that worked because a drunk waiter with diarrhea, though the exact one the customers deserved, would reflect poorly on the establishment. On the positive side I then felt free to retort hilariously to the callous tourists rudely demanding their food.

Being Paradise, mosquitoes did not live there, a condition I found jarring, being from Florida. It also didn't rain. I slept blissfully on the soft sand and was reanimated by the sun rising over the edge of the Sea into another day of pure fun. An even higher luxury was coming.

Weakened from intestinal woes but socializing at a table on the taverna patio, I began to notice her catty-corner from me crinkling her Aryan nose while grinning and staring at me beyond the point of reason and I judged her a bit mad. But when the blonde North German teenager led me around the rocks to recover on her dried seaweed bed, I found it delightfully comfortable. She branded me with my first and only ankle bracelet and dubbed me Sand and Sea for the green flecks in my green eyes that had arrested her; who would one day run up a Florida beach to me crying from the beauty of the dawn, so that I feared she had been attacked.

I was given the opportunity to breathe through a cigaret in Greece. I worked one day for a man who powered his small boat between islands collecting discarded soda bottles of European tourists, to sell. As we bounced along in the chill morning air, he ignited a cigaret and offered it to me in the bow. I declined and thought I was within my rights. He still offered it, assuming I had misunderstood his gracious gesture, thinking perhaps he was just showing me what a good cigaret he had. When I continued turning him down and he came to realize that I knew exactly what I was doing, he was absolutely thunderstruck. He could neither reconcile in his mind nor continue to live on a planet where a man would refuse such a boon from another man as a cigaret to breathe through. So one hand on the outboard's tiller, he stretched forward with the other desperately trying to force it on me. Perhaps he assumed me a European, who always can be seen practicing with such things.

When I finally realized what I was doing to this Greek and his world view, I allowed mercy to prevail. To his enormous relief, I took the wondrous gift from his fingertips, still smoldering, and breathed through it. I learned quickly that exhaling through a cigaret is as impractical as inhaling. That was more than enough for me and it was my next European trip before I bothered to breathe through another one.

Fall and spring peddling brought more extra money so the next summer it was hitching and fly- fishing around Ireland. Pretty much the opposite of thumbing in the U.S., everyone was articulate and entirely up on current events. In spite of this they were confused by the events, not sure who was responsible for what regardless of who claimed it. Everybody thought Catholic versus Protestant was nonsense.

In Wales I stayed at a creepy B&B as did the recent Miss Rose of Tralee from New Zealand. She told me how she had just come off a frustrating year living with an uninspirable Englishman. That night she got accosted making her late-night toilet by the old Frankenstein who lived there. I awoke to her yelling as he tenaciously pushed open the door, she steadfastly matching him from her porcelain throne. One would think she'd have appreciated his zeal. Someone eventually came and got him.

Contrary to myth, U.S. truckers almost never pick up hitchhikers but they're great for it in the U.K. I received my first ever thumbing transfer heading for Belfast. To keep me safe, from what I don't know, a trucker called in a hand-off to another trucker for the final leg. That was pretty sweet. In Belfast even going to

Woolworth's everyone was frisked.

In Newtownyards, a suburb of Belfast, Dennis and Heather's house is large, specifically so folks can drink and crash without the car. My showing up set off a party that ended six days later with a drive to the ferry to Scotland. Squeezed into the middle was a rare sunny day when we took a drive up the lovely Antrim coast. Allison came along sans her ex-boyfriend.

Dennis was the apotheosis of rambunctious, first wrestling me by the road when I got out the car, and winning, then more memorably suddenly reaching from the front seat to the back, up Allison's dress and pulling down her underpants, proclaiming joyfully, “I've got Allison's knickers;” meeting with some resistance but Dennis prevailed there also. Call me easily surprised but I've never gotten over my surprise at that. Had to go to Ireland to see it, so maybe that's a funny thing energetic men do there in front of their wives. By his proficiency I'd say Dennis was practicing in the classroom when he was nine, on any lucky girl whose desk was behind his. And my teachers thought *I* was out of control.

On the morning of my last day, we're all sitting around some downstairs room in a strange and sickly state of suspended animation way beyond hungover but almost certainly shy of dead, nobody knowing what to do or even willing to try to do it anyway. In our hands we each have a shot glass recently filled by Dennis which nobody wants to empty into himself. We're staring at it like it's hemlock. It looks like the party's over and then slowly, heroically, Dennis begins again. Later that morning they drove me to the ferry to Scotland.

I hitched from Scotland through Wales en route to a rendezvous across the English Channel with the maiden of the seaweed bed. I got off the ferry and saw her walking with some guy so I walked alongside them listening to her fret about how she hadn't seen me and she didn't think hitchhiking was such a great way to catch a ferry, etcetera and then she took a closer look at the other person walking beside her. It was pretty funny.

We hitchhiked down to a Spanish island famous to Germans called Ibiza and I found out how easy is hitchhiking in Europe with a girl with long blonde hair. Doesn't really make sense. Do they think they're going to borrow her? Stupid Europeans.

Petra could speak more languages than Santa Claus so she would talk to the driver, then I would ask what they said which meant she was always going current language to German to English which she found exhausting after a while.

Since we could afford to be picky, I insisted we put out our thumbs only to pick-up trucks for panoramic viewing. Petra violated that edict immediately and I was pretty annoyed. Before I could stop her, some hopeful European guy had slammed on his brakes and we had to be in a car again for awhile. Back of a truck, hands down best way to see Europe.

We camped alone on a low cliff overlooking the sea and laid out under the August meteor shower without getting wet. All day every day I was snorkeling in the crystal Mediterranean, occasionally climbing out on a rock like a seal. In the evening I caught ingredients for fish chowder and the seaweed maiden serenaded us on her octopus guitar. It was ridiculously satisfactory.

I learned that even popular destinations like Ibitza go largely unexplored as the tourists gather to see each other in one spot. Most of that lovely island rimmed with reefs was deserted.

A few years later my Irish-American Mom and her cousin went to Ireland and had a wonderful time with the Pattersons.

8

Always I wanted to visit Mars and Africa, the one I had seen for years but couldn't reach and the other whose fantastic existence I had to accept on faith, but was reportedly only a hop, skip and a jump away.

In 1981 a cryptozoologist from University of Chicago (if you're like me, this reminds you of that old saying, "What the hell is a cryptozoologist?") was organizing an expedition into the Congo because some pygmies he knew claimed to have seen brontosauri livin' in them thar backwoods (or maybe he stretched things a tad to inspire donors). I had read it in the paper and wanted desperately to tag along. He ignored my calls but at 8:00 one morning I caught Roy Mackal answering his own phone at the university. I beseeched him to make me part of the team. Saying I was a photographer piqued his interest a little but zeal wasn't enough. Clearly misunderstanding whom he was talking to, he said twenty-thousand dollars could make it happen.

"So," says I, "I'll have my own trip to Africa."

I was lucky this Africa expert hadn't been won over by me. I later read that his native guides abandoned him deep in the jungle, the expedition turned out a disaster and nearly fatal and they saw no dinosaurs. Sounds to me like he was a victim of over-preparation. I too saw no dinosaurs and my trip also was nearly fatal on an almost regular basis, but it was a life-enriching experience enabled by the near suicidal ignorance that pointed my way. Not to have gone would have been the disaster.

My goal was East Africa and I planned to get there cheap: the less you pay, the longer you can stay, as they say. Freddie Laker, a hundred bucks and a DC-10 got me to Gatwick Airport in typical Laker style, amid the mock enthusiastic applause of the drunken passengers. Because English customs workers decided to hassle me for a couple hours, by the time I walked out the train station into the London bleakness, it was too late for a room, yet I was shocked by my good fortune. Across the street idled a Greek bus and I knew for a fact Greece was on the way to Africa. Athens was forty bucks away and things were falling into place.

Despite the past two summers my grasp of Europe's length hadn't improved much. I thought someone said it would take 24 hours. That was alright by me. I could do that standing on my butt without sequitur.

We already were underway when I more correctly heard it would be *three* 24 – hour days. I almost got off. Bad hitchhiking usually beats sitting on a bus for three days. However I'd already hitchhiked down Europe twice and neither time could I manage to miss France.

You may be one who buys as I did, the popular portrayal of the French as a life loving, joyous people driving around with their tops down, ascots flying in the wind and reveling in every ray of sunshine that bears down upon them. This, dear readers, is a vicious lie. No Frenchman worth his paprika would squander good second hand smoke in this manner.

In France, no matter how glorious the weather, the indigenous drivers keep their windows rolled up tight, smoking. This is why a French motorist would rather watch a hitchhiker wither day after day by the road like an uprooted plant, until he drops dead, than give him a lift. He is loathe to risk by opening the door the escape of any of this precious environment he has striven all day to trap for himself, even worse having to share with a stranger whatever remains. The Frenchman would more likely pull alongside and butt out his cigaret in the luckless wayfarer's eye than grant him a ride. This action would require only the partial opening of a window and to blind a tourist would afford him some pleasure to cover the loss of cigaret smoke.

If you would stand with a cigaret clearly displayed showing your ability to contribute, your chance may improve. But really, you don't want them to pick you up anyway. So the thought of struggling one time more through France kept me seated and I was not sorry.

The joviality of the roster forestalled tedium until the breakdown of civility in the final twelve hours; except the head driver, a charmless inconsiderate tyrant over his tubular rolling realm who never approached civility. His repugnance would strain the vulgarity of an Australian. Apparently this is unavoidable. In speaking to the seasoned European traveler, you need say no more than "Greek bus driver." The picture is complete.

With a theme similar to more sinister events later in my vacation, our infuriating host stopped at every roadside eatery between London and Athens, where most of his flock followed him in to pay through the nose for a smidgen of grub and he took his kickback and free excellent looking meal. And then he tried to leave behind anybody not ready and on the bus when he was. This strutting bucket of rancid olive oil seemed to like me even less than everyone else, probably because my opinion of him was never in doubt.

Unfortunately we had paid up front. The terrible cartoon could rant and rave at us to his heart's desire. Except for a jovial fellow from Crete, whom he never abused, we couldn't recognize a word he was shouting; and it was his ball and he was taking it home with us or without. He never counted heads on re-boarding.

The language barrier left us no effective way to retaliate, as if he were surrounded by a force field repelling decency. However, displaying the kind of initiative suspected to lie solely in the domain of Americans, I devised the solution.

Since my time in Greece two summers previous, I had

suspected the spoken Greek language of being gibberish and nothing more. That is how it sounded to me and so, I thought, that might be exactly what it is. And why not? In the simple life of Greece, this should do. The Greek speaker lets fly some gibberish and by his voice it is judged if he is happy or not. When you boil it down, that's all anybody anywhere is trying to say: “I'm happy” or “I'm not happy – fix it.” Elsewhere this statement is veiled in innumerable nuances of language. The Greeks are not less guileful, just less patient.

The Greek man will not wax eloquent about whether or not the octopus has true intelligence, and then tap his toes while the object of this speech divines his feelings. Even if he did, he'll never know if she got the message or if she gives a fermented baklava, already conveying *her* mood with recipes for the eight- armed intellect in question. So to avoid this drama, he blurts a torrent of gibberish with an inflection that leaves no doubt about his state of mind. His purpose achieved, he is free to go about other business. Truly it is an excellent system.

The chance came to try my theory and I achieved a result that, I believe, indicates merit. Per my custom I was the last passenger to re-board at one of our never-ending stops. This was to stretch my legs as long as possible and to irritate the driver. He met me on the steps of the bus and spewed one of his gibberish admonitions at me. I got right in his face and and flung at him an explosive volley of my own angry gibberish: something on the order of “Abadablayabadabdabdbabadabagortlesnorkabayabadabadoo.” Really fast. He shut up and stared at me for a moment with a most stratified look on his fat face. Then without another sound he turned and took his seat behind the wheel.

I wish I knew what I said because I know damn well he got it. Maybe gibberish is an actual language. I had no more trouble with him and he was less obnoxious to the other passengers for the duration of the trip.

Passengers I remember were: a pleasant young French guy, [*] a young butcher from England named Mike, rather conservative as one might expect, a middle-aged personified ego from Crete with whom it was fun to trade insults, two teenage English girls and a blonde, blue-eyed sixteen-year old boy model brimming with desire for others of his sex.

At the point in the story where the bus breaks down, it did so. Luckily the English lasses were well equipped for such an emergency. Unluckily Heather and the intoxicating beverage didn't cohabitate well and she threw up in her seat which was right behind mine.

I was learning that being the American on the bus imbues one with pick-up truck loads of appeal. The girls and the boy had their caps set for me. Too bad it was the boy pressing his case early on. Whene're I exited the bus he followed, pelting me with pretty proposals as I propelled myself to my particular destination which usually was a bathroom. He was way too indelicate about his personal preference and by day three the bus air was permanently permeated by nasty catcalls between him and some of the more

---

[*] The reader is examining closely the unusual proximity of the words "pleasant" and "French." And I suspect he is further noting the two concepts in one sentence. It is no typo. That is how I recollect the individual. Historically when one makes an unbiased report as I do here, the public may be inclined to challenge his competence. This is a truthful narrative and I have striven to present things as I found them, however fantastic. Please remember that the platypus was declared a fraud when first sent stuffed from Australia to England. The writer hopes his veracity has not been impugned by the admittedly groundbreaking nature of this characterization of a Frenchman and that the reader will carry an open mind throughout the rest of this story.

Of course in starting out with such an improbable observation, I have gambled that the reader will not regard with a distrustful eye all that follows. I warrant the civilized imagination will not be stretched again to such degrees in these pages. In my defense let me state that I do not commonly take a stand that rages with such force against the laws of nature and I do not do it lightly here. And let me further state I cannot be sure the fellow wasn't lying about his national origin, although the idea of someone claiming France when it isn't true likewise strains the limits of cognition. No one is that humble. I do not like to belabor a point. When it's done, it's done. There is no profit in beating a dead brontosaurus.

conventional males. As a civilization we lasted two and a half days.

In Athens a few of us maintained contact and we enjoyed the nightlife, together cruising the bars, my favorite featuring bouzouki music and dancing. In one excellent place I led an entire long table full of foreigners in a chorus of *Why Don't We get Drunk and Screw* with the Coral Reefers backing us up from the jukebox. Although Heather was my only truly ebullient participant, it was, I like to think, one of the cultural low points of Greek history.

I slept on the rooftop of George's, comfortable more than the pricier rooms below owing to heat and humidity. The English girls vied that night for a position beside me and Heather won based on effort. A more magnanimous man would have provided for them both but I didn't really think it through. Also on the roof a morose young English couple night and day sat up against a short wall as if they'd been crucified there by Margaret Thatcher. My best guess was, here we are in Greece and one of us, you s.o.b., has herpes. It seemed they couldn't have been more miserable but Heather's presence did the job, forcing puss from the pimple of their festering lives. Through the night we received scolding and innuendo referencing farm animals to where I was forced to make some references of my own.

In the morning some friends of Heather visited and she made certain of being in violation as they had their conversation, no doubt assuring talking points for later on.

The reader may be noticing my proximity to Pelekas, beach of a million breasts and as many buttocks, endless frisbee and no mosquitoes I discovered two years prior. I am not even tempted by it. Stop looking at me that way. This is the danger of destination. It erodes judgment.

When I mention a Danish ferry, it must evoke in the untraveled reader a small, blonde, flying woman who materializes at night to furnish a breakfast danish under our pillow. For me it was the means of going Athens to Crete where I had to wait eight days for something comparable to Alexandria; but visiting Crete for eight days may be some people's idea of a vacation so I tried to make the best of it.

When the ferry hit Heraklion, I had the prescience to get off, cementing the semi-final leg of my headlong rush to Africa. Then I flamboyantly rented a car and invited Mike, whose destination was Crete, and Marian and Koos, a Dutch couple from the boat to come along and pay what they would. I drove over as much of the island as possible in one day and was told I was a typical American for doing that. I don't get it because I'll bet most Americans have never even been to Crete. But it's a compliment I have received many times, always with humility. Ironically I never feel like a typical American in America yet this is how I'm unfailingly perceived overseas. I suppose that demonstrates the utility of stereotypes.

I slept atop the Cretan Sun Hotel. Soon tiring of city life, I visited another part of the island where nestled a lovely beach called Vai to sleep on under the cool sheet of the full moon. Also featured were jiggling reflections, small colorful wooden boats moored just off the beach, rock outcroppings, Canadian nurses (so I knew healthcare was assured) and everything.

Now I feel the need to digress two years and dredge up another arrival to better illuminate my state of mind as the Dark Continent began to look like a distinct possibility. The saying "Be careful what you fish for" comes to the fore.

The loneliest I ever felt was walking off the plane my first time in Europe. What do I do now? Where do I go? What does one do in Europe and what in mama's pajamas am I doing here anyway? These questions were returning with greater force as I approached Africa.

One problem was nobody to ask who'd been to these places. I found fault with calling Europe a continent because on the map it was just the west coast of Asia. Africa, now that's a continent.

I would have felt hardly less ease with Mars looming before

me. At least on Mars you can see where everything is. I knew a little more about Africa than Europe, probably because they didn't stand up art and literature around it. I envisioned getting on and off safari buses to Mt. Kilimanjaro and the Serengeti Plain in Tanzania. I hoped to see a rhinoceros, which would be closer to seeing a triceratops than what's -his- name was going to come. I was curious about South Africa and I wished to see with my own two eyes the famous Egyptian pyramids. And I would have as soon leaped into a wood chipper as set foot in Uganda. How any of this was going to be realized I had no clue.

It was simple fear of the unknown and even I knew there was plenty of that. Europe was bad enough but Africa had a whole lot more.

Five days after my Egyptian visa arrived I was on my way, cutting it so fine I had to pick up my stamped passport in the Miami Airport. Laker's policy of all seats being stand-by made that possible.

I left the U.S. equipped with an Ethiopian visa also, which lay fallow for the whole trip. A South African visa was denied for I had given my occupation as photography. Customs mistook peddling laser prints for the dreaded “photographer” which I was no more than any tourist. This failure benefited me. It turned out such a visa would have denied me Kenya and Tanzania. Evidence of the application and denial stamped in my passport went to my credit at border crossings and smoothed the way, which smoothing I usually was in need of.

Had I given myself more notice, I might have done some research. As it was, I wound up frantically searching for my absolutely essential frisbee and unable to find it.

It was a great travel frisbee, a Humphrey Flyer actually, like a flattish flying saucer. Relatively small diameter, it fit snugly into my backpack and, of course, doubled as a plate. I had found this yellow disc with my toes one day as I waded around Lake Claire fly fishing. Its highly improbable resurrection was significant because there was a good frisbee lying in watery exile forever, so near to spring days and smiling faces, yet unable to rise from the sand bottom of a lake to join the fun. Since our providential meeting it had flown over Europe in two summers, over the Rockies and over Mexico and Belize. I was proud to have cheated fate in this way and I loved to add new localities to the Flyer's flight log. Double the remorse I could not completely kick the ass of fate and add Africa.

The new ferry arrived in Crete and during the crossing to Alexandria I teamed up with the Dutch couple, a German named Alfred with an earring (a noteworthy adornment in those days) and a French guy named Paul. Actually he wasn't too bad either*.

I was reconciled to arriving in Africa like David Livingstone, with neither frisbee nor clue. However, during the voyage I noticed Marian and Koos poring over an astonishing book. Everything changed when I discovered *Africa on the Cheap,* a travel guide apparently designed for me. It was thick as a baseball bat's sweet spot and packed with vital information I would not have and it crippled me. I couldn't imagine continuing without it.

My world view had been transfigured and I looked out across the vast gulf between being without because you ain't got no frisbee and being without because you haven't the book. An overview existed but I would be groping along aware of only what was in front of me. Never had I dreamed there could be so much not to know.

Though the couple were going only to Egypt, they refused to sell this cornucopia. I set myself to memorizing as much as possible and scribbling the indispensable. This was performed in a panicked fury as Egypt drew near. Had the voyage been longer with enough paper, I'd have copied the whole thing.

Once in Africa I never met a traveler without it. I suppose the existence of such a guide may have inspired them to go. And what

---

* Hey – I'm sorry. It was a heck of a year for Frenchmen.

a goldmine of misinformation it turned out to be. I have since seen other travesties of Australia's Lonely Planet Press, which, while trying to stay current and off the beaten path with reports from travelers on the ground, produced books abundant in outdated and sometimes dangerously inaccurate advice. It was trying to be the internet without the technology. In an eerie way it presaged the homogenized era to come. (This does not apply to present day Lonely Planet, which inevitably blended in as metaphorically predicted in *Number Twelve Looks Just Like You.* Gone the way of Backpacker and Outside Magazine, it no longer aspires beyond Frommer's with hip language.)

The goal of Alfred, Paul and the Dutch couple was to find an oasis somewhere and then go sit by it or something. Being from Florida, where lakes are everywhere, I couldn't see the appeal but I guess for a European that's a pretty neat thing to do.

Marian and Koos had been to Egypt before and they brought away a tale of misery to tell: Koos, the male part of the team, had decided to hitchhike across the Sahara Desert so he could say he'd done it and, in my opinion, prove his manhood. This is what is left to a Dutch man unable to find a dike to plug. I thought it a shame to drag the girl along on the test but maybe it was for her to see it. Marian said, "We ran out of food and water. Finally we got a ride with a man in a very small car filled with luggage so there was barely room for us to jam in. He had no extra food or water so we sat up every night crying from hunger and thirst." (the untold story is how long they would have endured before trying to kill the stingy driver). Anyway, do you think they enjoyed that first cold drink? And all subsequent ones a little more?

At last! Alexandria! The final ferry docked and I stepped off her into Africa, proving that it really did exist and could be reached if you just keep going that way. In fact it probably would be hard to miss.

A Special Note to the Reader

I wish to correct a false impression that may have been conveyed in some earlier pages. The possibility exists, however slight, that the reader has been given the idea that I do not regard highly French motorists and Greek bus drivers. This simply is not the correct conclusion. I never am one to generalize about a subset of humanity. There are good and bad of all races and one needs only the skill to discern the difference. As soon as I see a good one, I'll do that.

In the meantime too much praise cannot be heaped upon all the French and Greek people who do not drive. This cannot be overstated. They have seen their duty to the world and they have done it.

Vai

EGYPT

Now I would find out what was going to happen to me in Africa.

Education commenced immediately. Between dock and city my companions introduced to me the glamorous "black market." Suddenly I was trading traveler's checks for Egyptian money with an old man in a small booth in a bazaar. All changed money save Alfred, whose currency didn't answer. Even an old man in a bazaar has some standards. Only pounds and dollars, currencies of the winners, would do. Alfred was indignant. I suppose he had imagined Germany an economic powerhause in the world, certainly not to be dismissed by such as this Egyptian. My pals assured me I was getting a good deal.

Beggars abounded but I never lost a nickel on them. In general they disgusted me. Two years prior in Venice I had seen a young woman holding captive across her lap a boy of eight or nine who should have been off running and playing, thieving, anything but that. He seemed to be drugged. Her body was whole so she used the boy for sympathy. I despised her for that.

I did weaken one time. A smudged little girl approached me with hand out. For the first and last time I couldn't say no. The total didn't meet her bar and she looked at the change I dropped into her palm as it were octopus guts. Apparently beggars *can* be choosers. Been hearing the contrary all my life and never thought to dispute it. This must be what they mean about travel being educational. I vowed then never to donate to another one. Alfred gave always to boost his Karma account. He was visibly disturbed when I told him the beggars get picked up at the end of the day by limousines and the others agreed that it was so. I had read it in National Geographic.

This was the first I'd heard about Karma. But I knew if I had one it must be in sad shape as it never had been attended to.

We got a room together for next to nothing which is what everything costs in Egypt. You can get amazingly close to nothing there and we had white-robed Egyptians bringing us tea and, my most enduring image, a black dial telephone of no conceivable use. Things were working out great. Even on a huge unfamiliar continent, life keeps happening in little manageable bits which lead to the next ones. Who needs the overview? It began to seem that Africa was just another part of my native planet. How could I go wrong? (Insert Shakespeare here.) This is a subject I would investigate in great depth in the coming months and become quite learned on.

An animated pile of rags appeared in the doorway of the Alexandria Post Office. On closer inspection it was an Austrian student on holiday who immediately joined our band. I never saw someone so thoroughly disguised in her normal garb. She was short and constantly thrown around by her pack which appeared to dwarf her. I felt that if the match lasted long enough, she would be pinned. Her pants and shirt were baggy and rumpled giving the overall impression of only air inside them, just some enchanted garments escaped the laundry basket. In its brief appearances her face seemed dirty but with hair hanging down in front of it, I couldn't be sure and then it would go away again. So much face did her hair hide in fact, that in a still photo one would wonder if it hung down from her scalp or up from her mouth. She was in Egypt to find some Bedouins to go hang out with until school reconvened. But first – she had a post card to mail to England which I suspect is still en route. The scene that ensued from this one small purpose of hers created for me a memory I have cherished.

Inge bought the card in Greece where its subject matter is

common. However Egypt is not Greece. The card depicts against a stark white background, a side view of Pan very prominently and in miraculous detail featuring his excited condition which dwarfs the rest of his body. She handed the card innocently across the counter. The woman who received it could not have looked more astonished if her own naked husband sporting this freakish appendage had grinned at her from the card and it had been handed her by Anwar Sadat. This fine Egyptian postal clerk had achieved maximum astonishment. I truly believe nothing could have produced a greater effect on her and hers still is the standard to which I hold all surprise. She stared in a kind of mute ecstasy at the card for awhile and then collected herself enough to lean forward across the counter and, gaping in amazement at Inge, she asked in her lovely Egyptian accent, indicating the addressee, "Is this a man or a woman?"

Bravely the Austrian replied, "A man." Apparently that was the correct answer.

It brought down the house. The clerk started giggling and howling and yelling for everybody to come look. Where they all were half a minute before was a miracle of storage and now a mob of repressed female Egyptian postal employees thronged behind the counter with arms outstretched, screeching and reaching for the postcard, the original employee cackling over it all, "It's to a man! It's to a man!"

Me, I have to admire anyone with that little regard for decorum.

We watched Pan fade from sight across a field of outstretched fingers. It's a slow system but one imagines things get there eventually. Or somewhere. They were expecting great things then so even my card featuring the stern face of a Greek singer aroused great interest.

Separating Egypt from Kenya was Sudan, Africa's largest country, requiring a visa and six weeks sacrificed to obtain it. Averse to Egypt for six weeks when I could be in Kenya instead, I booked Nairobi with Ethiopian Airlines departing Cairo in a week. I learned that one thing not cheap in Egypt is airline tickets to Kenya; especially since I was required to buy a round trip, whose return leg I never used. Perhaps with the sophistication I would have later on, the ticket also would have been cheap.

Inge said she was seeking Bedouins because she wanted to "find a real man." The Dutch woman Marian nodded her head in solemn empathy as she rejoined wistfully, "I know what you mean."

Never have I seen a crueler blow struck. In that moment a man was stripped of his pride by the tongue of his wife as efficiently as a lion's tongue relieves a zebra of its hide. A ringer for the paint can Dutch Boy except with brown hair, Koos had hoped until that off-hand but heartfelt comment that his pretty wife had *married* her a real man. Or at least thought she had. I watched him crash from jovial contentment into despair. He had hitchhiked across the Sahara Desert, hadn't he? What more could she possibly want?

I never had heard anything about a Bedouin being any more real than anyone else but maybe Inge thought it stood for Bed you in. Of course the irony is the women of these nomads probably crave a virtual man like Koos.

My companions were trying for government permission to visit an oasis. In Egypt, where people align their schedule with nature's instead of building legions of air conditioners powered by pollution, like in Florida, government offices open early, close all day and reopen at eleven p.m. Koos, Marian, Alfred, Paul and Inge spent an entire morning glancing agency to agency in a pinball machine called *OASIS*. Finally the lights went off and the bumpers became unresponsive. Unable to ricochet any longer, they slid ignominiously down the exit chute, whoever was working the flippers covered in glory. That afternoon we met and they related their experiences. The hopefuls intended to renew their quest that night.

Sure enough, at eleven o'clock the pinball machine lit up and they shot back into it, me along for the spectacle. The traveling we did in one night would have required a week except for two Egyptian lads who had taken charge of us. My pals would be sent across town by one government official only to be returned by the next to within a block of where they just had been, to see someone else who surely was the one to grant permission. Particularly exquisite was every official lamenting that he lacked authority to grant the permission but he did know who had it. Then they would see that man and he would say the same thing usually after acting like he *could* do it. This should seem familiar to anyone who has seen Monty Python.

Eventually the tormented tourists had exhausted the inexhaustible supply of government officials in Alexandria and my expectation of their failure was realized though better than I envisioned it. One o'clock a.m., the circuit completely run, they were advised that now they absolutely would be sent to *the* man who could solve their problem. They schlepped their basket of hope to that address and it looked promising, an impressive building with armed guard at the gate. I suspected that this was where the president of the world stayed.

The guards were inclined to repel us but after much discussion and dithering forth and back to the edifice, we were granted entry. Soon we stood in the august presence of the first man they had talked to that day, free to begin the cycle anew. His station in life apparently had risen during the afternoon; or he was just more important at night.

The United States government prides itself on red tape snafus but they are mere dabblers and with no art to it. In ancient Egypt bureaucracy has been perfected. Although game, the seekers were spared the second round. This time, after re-greeting them, the man revealed that it was impossible to get the hoped-for permission. Truly they had been striding toward a mirage. Maybe he knew they wouldn't accept the bad news first time around, in which case the system is kind, shedding upon their struggle the light of hopelessness by illustrating there is no escaping the cycle.

Egyptian students admired English and Americans, typically displaying these flags on either side of their lunch caskets. The brothers who adopted us had exerted themselves to help the oasis seekers, guiding them everywhere, even obtaining proper cab fares, even though they were neither nationality. Maybe they liked all foreigners but lacked the surface area to feature more flags.

They spent their free time with us at the hotel, content to sit quietly in such splendor. Being high-schoolers, one would have thought they could find better things to do. It shows you that everyone is a king. He has only to find his subjects. Their mute presence was overwhelming after a while but we were willing to endure it since we were guests in their country. You wanta play, you gotta pay. Except Alfred, whose strained goodwill finally was overthrown by his heritage. As all the world knows, to many Germans there is no being a guest in someone else's country. Indeed there is no thing such as someone else's country. He ran them off in a bellowing rage.

Learning the proper cab fares was a permanent boon to us all. It is not an easy clam to open. I remember the look of hurt on their faces and I still remember them as they asked of me in a note.

Things never were the same with the group after that. All were relieved the brothers were gone but not glad about the way it was accomplished.

We made one foray more down to the money changer. By now the storm trooper had armed himself with acceptable currency. Receiving some oversized bills, I expressed concern that they were real. By the reaction from my pals that must have really shown how ignorant and unsophisticated I was but I got the impression that my lack of pretense flipped on a switch in Inge. "Ah," mused I, "perhaps real men lack pretense."

Promising to meet at the Everest Hotel, I left my partners in Alex and for about 35 cents I made the 7 hour train ride to Cairo third class. It would have been cheap enough anyway but by changing money on the black market and claiming to be a student (that good old international student i.d. readily obtainable anywhere for four dollars) this is what I had whittled the price down to. Flamboyant fellow that I am, I weighed options and determined that for 35 cents it wasn't worth trying to thumb there.

I learned that my idea of third class had sorely lacked colour. In Egypt it means there are two Egyptians even dirtier than you are (though no dirtier than you will be) half in your lap from each side, the feet dangling in your face and kicking you in the head of the Egyptians ensconced in the overhead luggage rack (a perch I grew to covet as it had far better amenities than a seat. Those go fast. Looking back, that must have been the first class berth) and the constant opportunity to buy snacks and sodas from urchins striding up and down the bodies laying in the aisle (second class I suppose). And with all this humanity, nobody to talk to.

The Cairo suburbs had many homes memorable to see from my ever widening viewpoint. Most striking were indentations in a red-clay cliff-side with a new white car parked in front of each. If you want to add to your square footage, just grab a shovel.

As I checked into the Everest Hotel, my travails, I had thought, at an end, the clerk surveyed my passport entry stamp with dismay. A stricken look upon his otherwise Egyptian face, he told me, "It says here that you are a danger man."

My life experience led me to believe him. It seemed natural that my passport would be so stamped. The customs people must have somehow contacted my elementary school. He laughed on seeing that he had gotten me.

My eighteenth floor room commanded a fabulous view of the city and trains of which I took countless time-lapse night photos and my bed had bed bugs. I guess that's cheech and chong.

The Everest overlooks Ramses who in turn overlooks Ramses Square which, even for Cairo, is not fancy. One imagines the former Pharaoh wildly unimpressed with his current situation. A

Muslim holiday where they fast all day so they can enjoy gorging at night, Ramadan was in full swing so eats were scarce during the day. I guess when the food's this monotonous you have to get creative. Each night I took my meals with the locals, eating much falafel and something else and the cost equaled my train ride.

Cairo is crammed with every kind of ground conveyance known to man or woman, all vying for the same space. As I sat just off the street in my favorite eatery, I witnessed a goat – car accident. The car was backing over the goat with the apparent goal of pushing it into the eatery. The tied-up goat had no vote, leaving the car with no choice but to rearrange its bones. The proprietor saw it also and sadly shook his head.

Tourists will speak of Egyptian dishonesty but that is because they patronize only tourist oriented businesses or they have taken a cab. In the places where I ate it did not manifest. Indeed, one evening I accidentally left some change on my table and the proprietor ran after me to return it. This appraisal does not stretch to cab drivers who are not Egyptian or Greek or Italian. Dispersed as they are, they form their own despicable nation.

{Like rats, cab drivers thrive everywhere that civilization does; but research has shown that only a French woman will mate with one, having practiced already with French motorists. Since there are too few of these to satisfy the global demand, cab drivers have evolved a specialized means of reproduction. When the mood strikes, they simply climb into a sewer or a pile of garbage which recognizes and welcomes its own. The chemistry of this joyous union catastrophically creates a few new cabbies. They emerge from the putrid smoke and ooze that is their mother and set themselves upon the civilized world. It is a powerful incentive to limit access to these places.}

Each of my senses has kept a single, prevailing impression of Cairo. For my nose it is the inescapable, nagging odor of a urinal never flushed but past and presently used. In a way that is Cairo. You easily imagine the scent of the Pharaohs' stream still borne upon the air, unable to escape its historical significance.

The roads never reflect the sun or the moon from any section, so continual and close are the automobiles. If a ray of light dives to the street behind one car, it will be intercepted by what remains of the front bumper of the next before it can arrive. In seven days I saw seven collisions. Never is there a time not to honk, so in self defense every driver holds a hand on the horn from go to whoa (no one wants to be the only person not honking. One imagines he would be crashed into constantly). This cacophony is what my ears remember.

Vision retains a ragged woman perched atop a twelve-foot high pile of garbage on a city sidewalk and I feel my own sweat from the incessant heat and air pollution that is the Egyptian noodle soup of existence in that strange can of worms in the desert.

Cairo offers a few daytime recreations, problematic because one must somehow reach them. One such destination is Giza where the Sphinx and the Great Pyramid remain and which are revered by the locals so that, if you like, you may climb all over them and even chip off a piece for a souvenir. Though tempted, I did neither. Their ongoing presence testifies to how big they must have been originally and a certain lack of initiative from the tourists. Or for most of their thousands of years, when they looked better, locals took a keener interest in their preservation. The current surface is unsuited to artistic expression but at one time the hieroglyphiti must have been amazing.

Taken for granted at this point, it's a boring side show harkening back to a grand enterprise, interesting now only for its scale and our modern inability to imagine putting that much work into anything that doesn't make money; a tantalizing joke with its punch line lost in the times of sand. In ruin they are Wonders of the World. I wonder if they even were a decent tourist attraction in their heyday; goldbricking honed to a fine art over years of assembly, citizens debating if they'll ever get it done, like an Irish road crew leaning on their shovels around a pothole. And one must question if the same zeal operated at the end as at the beginning. Maybe it was the original New Deal. "What can we give these guys to do for awhile?"

The high point of my Giza visit was climbing up a narrow chute inside one of the pyramids and finding myself alone in the tomb of Cheops, of all the frickin' places. Imagination can really run wild there. You are alone deep inside one of the great man made wonders of the world and no distractions. You talk about safe. Cops out there looking for you, never gonna find you. "Oh, hey – maybe he's in the pyramid." I don't think so. Better than being underwater. Just remember to pack a lunch. (I didn't see the restroom. And in case King Tut or somebody is wondering, No way Akhenathan, I wouldn't do that. I imagine many tourists have dared the Mummy's Curse to make that claim to fame but not me.)

Standing there physically inside the past, your modern bladder holding its own splendidly, it's easy to believe you are an ancient Egyptian just awakened from an absurd dream about the 20th century. You have only to crawl outside to see that it was indeed a dream and you kiss the urine-enriched sand and thank whoever was God then that you are back in Kansas. Imagining things is fine but then I noticed the chamber accommodated an incredible echo. I sent forth in the ancient space a few pretty good belches in a row and had the once in a lifetime opportunity to hear them mingled into a trio as they toured the acoustically perfect walls of Cheops' tomb. One of the great Wonders of the World just got greater. This inspired my theory that the pyramids were built as a series of belching chambers where the Pharaohs could go to compete.

Another interesting way to while away your abundant time is to visit Mummies R Us, known officially as the Museum of Cairo, whose marble floors will waste your feet in no time and where you will learn that the Curse is real.

You may have the soothing impression that mummies are rare but a visit to this place will dispel that comfort, and the movie will infiltrate your dreams. Here you will find mummies laid out as far as the eye can survey, all sizes, all splendid. One becomes tired contemplating them. They are as ubiquitous as falafels and if you stay too long, as I did to beat the acrid heat, you will be unable to imagine a building without one (To this day, on entering an unfamiliar building I start looking for the mummy and am never comfortable until I've found it). There's a guard or two to ensure proper respect is accorded the exhibits and that you pay for any pieces you chip off. I thought a mummy was a rare thing but a mummy to an Egyptian is as common as deas are to a flog. I suspect they are status symbols and every citizen worth his waste shelters some, lack of at least a tiny mummy on the tv signaling abject poverty and initiating social disgrace.

A daily sight outside the U.S. Embassy was a crowd of locals all having the same impossible mummyless dream: permission to visit a vast oasis across the ocean. I of course was free to go there anytime but for them Mars was equally near. I always have been grateful the accident of my birth happened in North America.

Halfway through my Cairo week the rest of the team showed up, stayed one night and were off the next day to Luxor. The enchanted clothes had diarrhea. Oh well.

I cared little about going further south in Egypt at the time but now I wish I had so I would have a better impression. I have the idea of Egypt that a visitor to Baltimore and New York City has of Argentina.

My very best day in Cairo I managed to sneak into the closely guarded Nile Hilton (an oasis) and hang out by poolside. I was one for two at that.

There was no reason to carry to Kenya Egyptian mummy, I mean money, so I ate frequently and indiscriminately, including ice cream sold on the streets and kept cold by hook or by crook. It probably had been frozen and refrozen on a daily basis so not surprisingly, on the eve of my escape to Nairobi, I had pushed digestion a day too far. Cairo gave me a bon voyage party.

My deliverance from bedbugs, unrelenting heat and human waste odors was leaving at five a.m. with or without me. Without me would mean a new five-hundred dollar ticket and another week in MUMMY WORLD. I had planned to finish my tour at the Everest with different bedbugs on the lobby couch to avoid paying for another night and so the desk clerk would not forget to roust me in time. At midnight I was well beyond caring about missing some airplane and forfeiting the ticket money. I only was afraid I wouldn't die soon. I advised Henny Youngman of this but he cheerfully woke me at three anyway, no doubt with some hilarious one-liner. Being only partially awake, I thought I felt a little less amazingly horrible so I grabbed my pack. The giant double doors of that edifice regurgitated me doubled over and clutching the devils' amusement park in full swing in my diaphragm. Behind me my backpack thudded down the stairs, step to step until I reached the street.

There was no lack of activity; buses back and forth solid with humanity and covered in hangers-on as thick as bees on a hive, and cabs too. I staggered around Ramses Square like I was gut-shot trying to flag down a cab. Nothing would stop for me because, as I would learn, they hadn't yet twigged my potential. It was like a crummy dream and I began to feel the disheartening marriage of sick and invisible.

Although I couldn't hear it for the racket, time was ticking away. Now on the street I deeply wanted whisking away from that urinous city. After an hour of this mummypoop, a darn long time when you feel like I did, Hallelujah! One of those puss sucking, garbage blooded cabbies stopped. They must have been playing musical chairs around me and he figured I finally was about to die and be ripe for looting. With an altogether different agenda I hoped that if we hurried I still might make my flight.

I told him where to take me and he stowed my pack in the trunk of his cab. Then he drove briefly and parked under a dark bridge where he got out and joined his friends at a little fire to talk and talk and talk. Well, this was a surprise.

Maybe he forgot he had a fare. I asked from my seat that we go and he only squatted at the fire and laughed and his friends laughed. Rankled that he didn't even invite me to this good time, I demanded that we leave and got the same reaction. Then I twigged the game. He was cheating at musical chairs, having captured me prematurely and awaiting my expiration in his cab thereby ensuring salvage rights. I, however, did not want to play with a cheater and out of sheer perversity became determined to live. Hugely disappointed to abandon what I had thought to be salvation, I was mentally preparing to drag myself and my pack back to the square wherever that was and try for a better ride, futile gesture though it probably would be.

The driver left the lively jabber at the fire and approached the cab to assess my state of decay. I told him to take my pack out the trunk. He refused. I don't know. Maybe it's just me but when I get in a cab I expect to be the one who names the destination. I don't want the driver to stop at a potluck and wait for me to die and things. Indignation was making inroads on debilitating stomach cramps. Without food poisoning I'm more patient with people; but when his unpleasing mug appeared in the window and verbally abused me, that did it and I hit him with the door. I oozed out into the letter S and demanded my pack. Unafraid of S, again he refused. Stretching to the more imposing C, I managed a credible threat which clearly promised violence, or at least vomit.

From my observations, Cairovians don't hit each other. I'd seen them yell after traffic accidents until they were blue in the face, (going some for an Egyptian) but never did they come to blows. Perhaps without a general armistice it would be one constant city-wide brawl. On an agitation scale of 1 -10, most Americans stop yelling at about six and commence shoving, followed by dukes up and hoping someone will intervene and drag them apart (this peacemaker need be no more menacing than Angelo Dundee and remarkably he is able to accomplish the deed, the foes angrily clawing at each other all the while).

Egyptians can be at nine and still pelting each other with words – long after I expected to see contact; and here I was at two and done talking. Sunshine wasn't ready for some good old no-nonsense Jingoism. The next thing he did was get behind the wheel and drive me to the airport. For a parting shot he tried to get more fare than we had agreed to.

"Four bowen," he said, extending his eldritch hand. That's what I call an optimist.

Ethiopian Airlines was way behind schedule anyway. Wonder of wonders, I was at Cairo International Airport and overjoyed at the prospect of a modern restroom to be sick in for awhile, my standard for joy having become far more accessible of late. I went for it like a cab driver for a urine soaked dollar bill.

The walls were amply decorated with nasty hieroglyphics, and a good inch and a half of fluid covered the floor of my haven, with Egyptians on hands and knees worshiping in the solution. In the multipurpose section all stalls were occupied. I don't know what was going on in there but nobody was leaving. Maybe the occupants were trying to see the aquifer.

Noting my distress at this, an unusually burly Egyptian pounded on each door. When this tactic bore no fruit, he reached under a random door and unlatched it and without even a "Howdy Doody" opened it and yanked out the offender. Gratefully I took his place. Maybe my champion was the restroom attendant. I sort of got the impression he was hoping for a tip.

Next thing I remember is downing the best Alka Seltzer of my life on board the best plane. Cairo, I was happy to see, ended at the runway. The plane was clean and mite-free and the stewardesses were kind and the food and snacks delectable. So. Everything's going great!

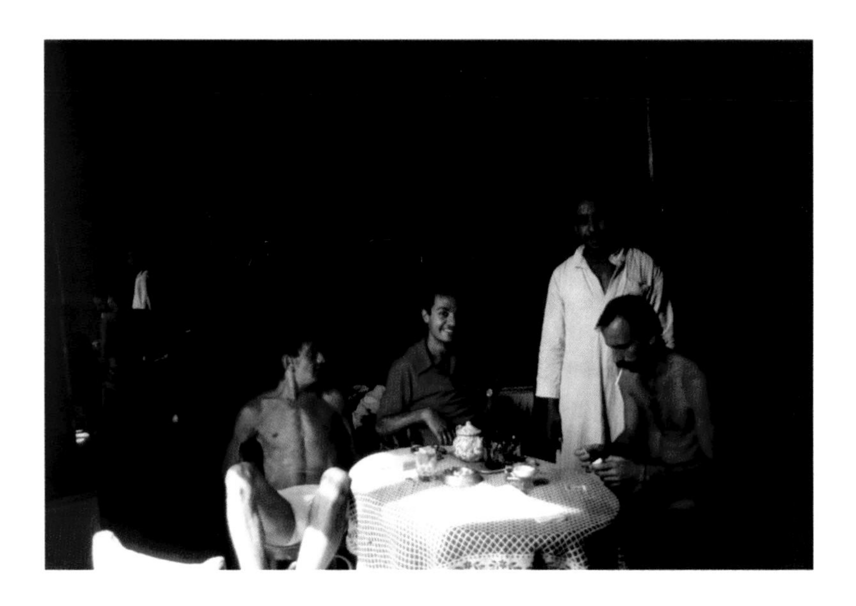

Frenchman, Egyptian kid, waiter, German

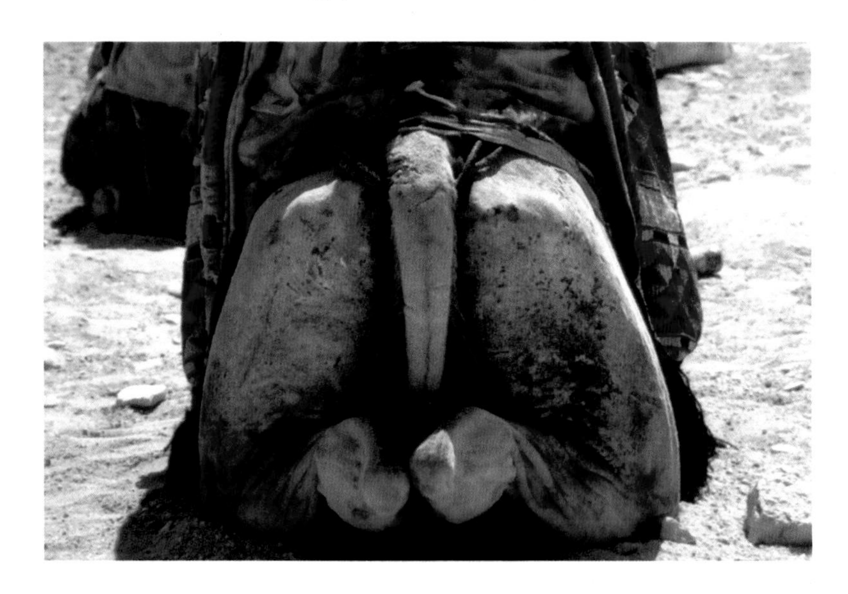

Egypt

Kenya or Ken'tya. That is the Question

If you can arrive in a place or make it to that place, I made it to Nairobi, the Kenyan capital, and directed my poor body to the nearest bed which I rented for twenty-four hours. From the extreme ice cream of Cairo arose a new man and eventually something sublime. I began to feel as a good dog would on finding itself at the hub of various indescribably delectable looking bones. Which one to go for first?!? In my case it was adventures, 365 degrees of them.

Once physically able to choose, I reverted to habit and lowered the rent. Someone directed me to my new base of operations. The Iqbal Hotel is a picturesque lodging preferred by the more discriminating tourist and the less affluent, often one and the same. Catering to the special needs of its patrons, the Iqbal offers an individual bed in a semi-private room or for those preferring a firmer sleeping platform, a space on the floor in the hall.

At the Iqbal I first pondered defecation East Africa style. In these crass times it could be a tv show. For the duration of my stay I never got it down, the pristine simplicity of the method and the true purpose of the water basin never dawning on me. As a game show, contestants supplied with the equipment would vie to be first to succeed with it in the intended manner. And the Iqbal is a hotel where one may be sexually assaulted while in the grip of a fever.

On the plane from Cairo I had met Tim Talbott and the magnificent Sheila Goldsmith, a young English couple that seemed not like a couple. The last of many unexpected lessons of this trip,

I would learn why at the very end, tying it up nicely.

Sheila's uncle lived in town and he drove us all around Nairobi National Park, just outside the city, where I saw my first giraffes. Then I knew for sure I'd gone someplace.

We saw baboons also and Sheila told of a South African couple that had stopped on the park road watching them. Their little daughter got herself out the car and they watched with one would imagine horror as the baboons dismantled her, never getting out to object. That kid must have been a real brat.

I felt right at home in Nairobi where I was declared more native than the natives. I regularly got fried fish at a little take-away joint and sat on the curb to eat it while receiving curious stares from passing locals.

Changing money with individual businessmen in lieu of banks is called, for want of a darker name, the black market. It's like a coupon for a discount on everything, available only to tourists. The catch is your paperwork won't jive with your cash, an issue at border crossings. This is where my denied South Africa visa application became a beautiful thing.

Who could resist? I planned to walk into a shop and stand around like something was on my mind and see if the proprietor took the hint. I struck paydirt right off in a jewelry store. The two Indian fellows were quite accommodating, offering a decent rate and no rhinopoop and they took traveler's checks which, I would discover, was not the rule, although they brought a slightly higher price.

Normally cash is the preferred item, in large denominations and good condition. I'm sure some of those guys would lose their minds over a brand new hundred dollar bill. And dollars and pounds are the ugliest money around. Not knowing I would be needing cash, I had brought very little so I was lucky to start with these jewelers. Soon I would learn how to remedy that problem.

As near as I could figure, if the economy of a country is weak enough, then its currency is useless in foreign exchange and the black market flourishes. Businessmen need dollars or pounds to buy with and they can't get them from banks or any other legal way except retail sales. As black market nations go, the Kenya economy was strong so illegally selling money was hardly worth the risk but it's hard to pass up a deal.

The bank rate was nine Kenya shillings for a dollar, black market about eleven. Eventually my contact declined traveler's checks. Luckily by then I had learned how to get dollars in Nairobi. If I could convince the bank that I was about to leave Kenya, they would cash as much as four hundred dollars in checks. I was able to convince them more than once, the key being my round trip ticket from Cairo.

One useful tidbit I gleaned from *Africa on the Cheap* was to reject anyone approaching me on the street to change money. Ostensibly their purpose would be to conk me on the head in a dark alley or get my money by slight of hand. The warning seemed sound. I was tried several times by seedy looking Africans promising outrageously high rates if I would follow them to the man with the money. I always loudly accused them of being thieves and wanting to hit me over the head and before long I got no more such offers.

I saw no beggars in East Africa. One day I sat at one of the long feeding tables in the Iqbal to eat a few doughnut-shaped things I had bought for a few cents. An African fellow already was at the table, sitting across from me. After a few minutes the young man asked me for one of my donut - shaped things, overestimating my humanity. He was not begging. He had simply asked me straight out if he could have one, a request that just about anybody else would have granted. I said, "No."

He accepted with dignity my reply and then he turned and left. But he did not walk away for he had no legs.

Well, poor me, I had a hard time enjoying my donut shaped things after that.

The Iqbal is a kind of mecca for hard core (financially

challenged) travelers. In my incomprehensible future my young son and I would be watching on tv a movie called Black Diamond set in South Africa. Except for at least one shot. They couldn't resist setting a scene with the Iqbal. I got all excited and said, "That's where I stayed in Nairobi!"

I noticed a neurosis of membership in the minority race. On seeing a white man I felt like greeting him as if we had a common bond, which we did. We were both probably tourists. This tendency began to feel oddly like discrimination and seemed silly and unsophisticated. So when passing an unfamiliar Caucasian ignoring me on the street, I often went out of my way to ignore him back. I wonder if Africans visiting Switzerland have a similar thing.

As all tourists at the Iqbal tend to meet, I met Terry Johnstone, a somewhat severe 23-year old from Napier, New Zealand. Like all from that country, he constantly bragged about the place, this sort of thing eventually pushing me there. Terry had paid his fare to Kenya on a Bedford truck with some other tourists. I guess the road through Sudan wasn't marked and they got lost in the desert, most of the passengers with hepatitis by this time. He said they were about to start drinking radiator water when the driver found the track. This is no worse than other stories I heard from people who crawled along under my Ethiopian Airplane, mingled also with accounts of the legendary hospitality of the Sudanese people when they met them.

Terry and I both felt like getting out of town, so with another New Zealander staying down on River Road in a crummier place than the Iqbal, we went camping in the nearby Ngong Hills. To Terry's disgust, his countryman didn't make it past Ngong Town. Terry felt that to give out like that was really "slack" and he took it as a reflection on himself. Concurrently he was proud that I seemed to have the right stuff (A few years later I would learn Terry held others to a standard of integrity higher than he required of himself.)

Probably it's good that my travel preparations are minimal because I prepare to my detriment. For example I didn't want my well used, excellent external frame backpack gift from Mom obstructing me getting on and off all these crowded safari buses I would be traveling on; so I had the great idea to buy a canoe pack, a big frameless canvas sack with arm straps, looked great in the store filled with foam rubber, something I could just swing like a cat if I wanted to. That's the curse of marketing for you. Full of real stuff it was like having a giant beer belly sticking out my back.

In the aptly named Ngong Hills I learned of my error in luggage, constantly trying new ways to lug my beer belly, none satisfactory for long. I even wrapped the whole mess in my sleeping bag and trudged along with that arrangement slung over my shoulder like Santa Claus on Christmas Eve. Every innovation was a momentary relief from the previous way and those my only moments of hope. Hope without salvation wears thin. Still, out of sheer perversity I always beat Terry to the top so my ego remained intact.

Too late we would learn that Ngong means knuckles. To grasp the frustration of these hills, lay your fists side by side and become a microbe scaling each knuckle only to lose all you gained dropping down the other side to begin again.

I recall surprise at seeing wildflowers wafting on the hilltops, flowers not in my preconceived notions of Africa. Always the flat Rift Valley spread out below us. Wind was perpendicular and steady and we saw the occasional hawk pinned up in the lift, not moving, just looking and enjoying the breeze.

Our final night we camped low among acacia trees. Some Masai spotted us and through the night, one at a time they walked silently up the grassy hillside to materialize from the moonless dark and sit by our fire. We hadn't yet picked up much Swahili so conversation stalled at greetings. It was a little awkward looking at each other, so much to discuss, so little to say. It must be how whales feel when people close encounter them. "Okay, here we all are. Now what?" We were frustrated and they were disappointed but we appreciated the attempt.

We thought each knuckle the last because you can see the next hill only from atop its predecessor. They were progressively taller or the valleys lower or it just seemed that way. At any rate we had found the world's slowest roller coaster. Gratefully we emerged on the far side of the fists pretty thirsty and we came to a hut. An engaging woman greeted us and gave us delightful cool water. We had a nice visit with her and she asked that we photograph her and send it to her. Terry would be the first one home so he took her address and agreed to do it.

More walking got us to a road and we hitchhiked to a nasty chemical lake where it's too hot, the air stinks and some exiles from Britain worked. They arrived there with their wives who already had buggered off. The only oasis was a kid-size clubhouse mostly filled by a snooker table. The men were serving out the sentences of their contracts, three years in the despair of a lonely, putridly boring existence. No woman had lasted beyond a few months. These, it seemed, must be men with very little choice.

I discovered that although it felt very fine and natural to be walking around Africa, many natives found it puzzling. I'm not talking Masai tribesmen but fairly urbane Kenyans. A policeman in this town of the chemical lake asked me, "Why are you on foot? Doesn't your government furnish you with a car?" and "Did you fly your own jet here?" No matter how I explained I had come for the fun of it independent of the government, and I was a regular Joe, it was all nonsense to him. He was a regular Joe too but he wasn't going to be traveling on his own dime to the United States to sight-see.

This was a valuable look at myself from the viewpoint of others. Maybe it was I who didn't get it, the absurdity lost on me of being in Africa by virtue of the invention of the airplane, my ability to buy a ticket and the leisure to use it; viewing it like a colossal diorama, having an amazing experience and then leaving with it in photos and memory to be cherished all my days, the friendship squandered of making friends never to be seen again; not as one who actually ought to be there, born there, with a stake in the place - home. Looking back, I was like the Coke bottle in *The Gods Must be Crazy* but less useful.

It was good to be able to up and leave that infernal place after only a few hours and bad for those trapped there. The people who had brought us were a white English family living on Kenya more than in it, isolated from native life; pure opposite of a Danish family I would meet later on. They let us know they had saved us from being picked up by Africans. Usually it's more important to be saved from English people.

Their lack of curiosity was something new to behold. The teen progeny in the car never had tried ugali, the staple and ubiquitous food made from maize meal and tasting a little worse than it sounds. They lived, they told us, in a fortified house with iron gates and an alarm system, a tiny inviolable island of England. I suppose this was a vestige of colonial days and a glimpse into the colonizers. Business concluded, they saved us again and returned us to Nairobi.

We ran into the disappointing New Zealander. He hadn't fared too badly in Ngong Town, having found a pair of fifteen year old girls to pass the time with. It sounded like almost as much fun as we had.

Back in Nairobi my dilemma was still intact – what to do? What to do? So I took a little day trip. I don't remember where – only the entrepreneur I met along the way. My transportation was a mutatu, a zany cross between a cab and a very small bus. An African man on board inquired of my destination and at a certain point in the ride said, "This is where you must get off," and he got off with me.

The mutatu left and there I was with this guy. A restaurant was nearby and he suggested we patronize it. He told me in a mocking tone, "Now you will see how the *real* Africans eat."

I sensed I should not have exited the mutatu as this obviously was not my destination. However I went along with the game and let my kidnapper play out his hand. He ordered ugali for both of us. I was dissatisfied with this view of tribal life and I had twigged his plan. He thought he had himself a dumb tourist who was going to buy him lunch. He was half right.

I gagged down my ugali and he relished his. We then approached the counter where he suggested I get some candy. I did and so naturally he took some also. Then I said, "Thanks a lot," and walked off. To my way of thinking, things don't work out much better than that. He looked so surprised and dismayed.

I was pretty irritated by that person and I blamed mutatu drivers in general for my inconvenience; so when the next one came along I felt justified in demanding a free ride. I was obliged. When you're hot, you're hot.

Still a man without a plan, I considered flying to the Seychelle Islands for a hundred bucks. Due to rumors of a coupe happening and strict regulation of where you stayed there, I opted out. At the time I didn't realize exactly what I was opting out of. I have since gotten a better idea of it and regretted deeply that decision. That was before the coral died from warming ocean. That would have been something. Instead I purchased a Kenya road map, something no other tourist I met had thought to do. They always looked at it hungrily. I never had heard of Mt. Kenya before and some American guys at the Iqbal hoped to climb it so I thought about doing that but it always was shrouded in clouds. I was surprised to find the Nairobi climate a lot like London, tending toward cool and dismal. It's like the invaders brought their own weather.

Flying into Nairobi the white Kenyan man seated beside me had advised that if I went to only one place, it should be some lake whose name I had forgotten. My dilemma was cured in a bookstore when I read the words "savagely beautiful." The writer was trying to describe Lake Turkana. I recognized the name the man had recommended. Only after getting back home would I remember that this lake and I had a history that went way back and indeed it may have induced my trip to Africa.

Meanwhile the Energy Conference had descended upon Nairobi with delegates from across the globe. The first subject addressed was the firewood shortage in the third world. I suspected this a token nod toward the host country but later I would appreciate its significance.

Two delegates got more than they expected, I'll wager. Or less. The man and woman were driving to a fortified home in Nairobi, maybe even the bastion of the folks Terry and I met. They were followed by "African hostiles" hoping to swap cars. Maybe the pursuers were about out of gas. When the white people pulled into the driveway, the Africans hemmed them in. The Africans got out the car and demanded likewise. The man obeyed and the woman cleverly locked her door and remained unmoved. So they shot her dead. Then she got out.

I wonder if colonists ever described themselves as English hostiles.

First giraffes

On the Ngong Hills above the Rift Valley

Lake Turkana

Here's the part where the writer embarks on a wonderful, unexpected jaunt to the dawn of mankind. The unlikely occupant of a two-hundred fifty mile around gash in the desert near the confluence of Uganda, Ethiopia, Sudan and Kenya, Lake Turkana is so remote from western civilization that it lay undiscovered by German tourists until 1872. Legend says it is a long lost piece of the Nile based on some common fishes. Having yielded possibly the oldest known human bones, this area is supposed by many to be the starting point for our species and thus, the beginning of the end for the passenger pigeon.

A road reaches up to its west side and a questionable track to the east so the east side was the obvious choice. Thumbing seemed impractical so I wished to reduce the cost of renting a four-wheel drive Suzuki. At the Iqbal feeding table, amid ragged Africans and the mouth-juicing aromae of Arabic grilling, I convinced a thirty-eight year old German glass blower-school teacher to come along. When it was over, he proclaimed it the best thing he'd done while in Africa. I know there were times, though, when I made Irmin Opper sorry he'd ever left home.

For a couple hundred dollars I rented the car at Central Auto Rental in Nairobi, run by Indians, no credit card needed. They related some interesting news; one aspect of which diluted my appetite for the trip and one which whetted it all the more.

"It is very dangerous up there right now. You should hire an Ethiopian Shifka to guard your camp while you are in that area."

The good news was, "Two fellows such as you hired a car

from us three weeks ago. As they drove along the Ethiopian border, a Shifka with a machine gun blocked their way. He wanted their portable radio and offered to trade a rock he claimed was gold. They decided, 'What the Hell. We'll do it.' On returning to Nairobi they had the rock checked. Indeed it was gold and worth about thirty-thousand dollars."

That must have been some radio.

I didn't bore Irmin with these stories, feeling he would find little in them of interest.

We brought extra jerry cans of gas and I stocked no food, confident of ambushing it in the lake and happy to procure snacks in villages along the way. Though I had heard nothing about the fishing in Lake Turkana, as isolated as it was, I figured it had to be great.

So began Irmin Opper's trip, a rare opportunity to see "the road not taken." That was exactly the route of this trip for him, for surely he was not supposed to be on it.

I had made another decision also; to get to the famed Serengeti

Plain via Uganda, the one country I thought I never would enter. This route was enforced by the border closure from Kenya to Tanzania. Terry Johnstone was heading for South Africa and home and also had no choice but to cross Uganda. He got hired to drive a safari truck to south Kenya and we expected to return from our trips about the same time so we made a pact to dare Uganda together. Thoroughly dreading the prospect of that country in the wake of Idi Amin, we each were glad for the company.

The New Zealander who saw greater potential in Ngong Town than in the knuckles wished to go with Irmin and me but his expected money failed to arrive in time. Unfortunately he told an Australian woman about the trip and we agreed to let her come along, getting the cost per person down a little more. However it wasn't worth it. In retrospect he probably was hoping to get rid of her. She was very proud that she had been already six weeks in Africa.

Our vehicle had a passenger and a driver seat and behind those, luggage space. It meant that we each would spend one-third of the time riding in the back on the packs, which didn't seem so bad talking about it. That meant a whole two-thirds of the time in a seat. I must have seen too many of those Dan Daily "two guys and a gal" movies. In practice it was miserable as was she, as are most Australian women who travel. At some time the country must have set adrift a load of undesirables. But my powers of appreciation pale next to Irmin's. He desired her.

Throughout the trip I saw him grasping for what in every way was the booby prize; and always he was disappointed because it eluded him. It brought to mind someone lamenting that he can't pick up a fresh turd because it's too slippery.

It is easy to fall into the trap of locating Lake Turkana not in geography but in time. Going places little affected by the Industrial Revolution is often called a trip to the Stone Age. This reflects an egocentric belief common among modern people that time cannot proceed without a leg up from our technology and it is indeed gadgetry that gives us a future and its absence that mires others in a timeless continuum.

Ours is a simple society of built-in obsolescence annually punctuated by changing car styles and computer capabilities. If the Turkana are living in the Stone Age then so are we.

Anyway, our little car hurtled us to a time before civilization, to the Stone Age itself, making us visitors from the future with inconceivable inventions.

Yes, it's an easy trap.

The road was paved immediately outside Nairobi, a condition we would miss from time to time. We took our first supper together at a restaurant in the town of Nyahurruru and had a very friendly chat with a local school teacher. We camped beside the gigantic, red Thompson Falls (for lack of a better name). My tent being the only one, the Australian woman suggested she share it but out of sympathy for Irmin, I condemned her to sleeping in the Suzuki with him.

Irmin had been to South Africa and he told of a bus he was on: "An African man was overtaking the bus on his little motorbike. One of the passengers stood at the side door and when the man pulled even he kicked him over. All the passengers laughed."

"Did you do anything about it?" I asked.

He said he would have feared for his own safety if he had.

Owing to the drag produced by my companions, we had three days more to Lake Turkana. Towns were scarce so after the first night my fellow adventurers liked to latch onto it if we came to one rather than be caught out in the countryside and have to camp again. The road was too bad to drive at night. This squandered heaps of travel time at the nicest time of day. Then every morning I had to climb the walls as they calmly sat and sipped their tea, without which infuriating ritual they would be unable to live a whole day, apparently. And why, I pondered, did they bother to do that?

In the vicinity of the village of Borogoi Irmin displayed one particular aspect of his character. I intend to describe it with a valuable communication method I observed in Africans.

I never heard an African use a slang derogatory term. They didn't call anyone nonsense like asshole, shithead or even jerk; instead they made a useful observation. For example "George Zambutu will eat your baby then pick his teeth with its bones." This has told me something important of Mr. Zambutu; especially if I'm looking for a baby sitter, far more than "He's a real son of a bitch." Or they might say someone else is "not a friendly person," instead of "a real asshole," like I might say. Obviously it is anatomically impossible to be an asshole real or virtual. But it is quite possible to be an unfriendly person.

I was shown a far more accurate way of speaking than my own and that of many of my fellow Americans including Richard Nixon. This caused me to ponder why we confide in this stupid way. I concluded that it is a means of elevating oneself (He's in the category of 'asshole' and I'm clearly not). Slandering him like this we chip away at the object's humanity believing we have done him harm. Also the object of our speech learns that if he loses favor, we might tell others that *he* is an asshole. I don't know why East Africans would be above all this unless they're just smarter. I am sure that describing someone as an asshole only makes a statement about myself. As Mom would say, "If you can't say something nice,...."

Irmin Opper was an uncoopperative man.

Rotten luck it was for me and the Aussie bitch (the reader sees how easily one may backslide) that Mr. Opper was driving as we approached Borogoi. The road dipped among some trees as it passed through a shallow stream. I never had seen a monkey outside a cage and I was outta my skin.

{I would like to say in fairness to myself that I may have called a sticky wicket a bitch but never a person, or even a dog for that matter, even before the example of the Africans. That was to give the reader a little chuckle after all that lecturing. I didn't mean it.}

"Stop the car," I yelled. "Look! There's monkeys!"

Does the reader think he would stop the car? A simple combination of clutch and brake pedal?

"Irmin," I said, "Those are my first monkeys. Turn the car around."

He kept driving away from my first monkeys saying in his ridiculous German accent, "There will be lots more monkeys."

I told him I didn't care about the next monkeys. I wanted to see *those* monkeys. It was as if my request merited no consideration at all. Like I was just tearing off my clothes and raving out the window. Maybe he was hoping I'd kill him. I don't know. It certainly seemed warranted. There were no more monkeys and to this day, thanks to Mr. Irmin Opper, the only monkeys I have seen in the wild are expatriots on Florida's Silver

River descended from *Tarzan* extras.

Borogoi was the first unmodernized village along our route as all thereafter. We had heard that if you stop in Borogoi, some super-friendly locals will place nails under your tires so you will get a flat one and stay longer. I'm thinking there's a few chambers of commerce that could learn something from Borogoians.

When we reached the village, the Aussie was nearly as excited about seeing her first wild natives as I had been about seeing her family. Again, would Irmin hit the brakes? It would have been easy enough to check for nails or just guard the car but still he blasted on through with the Aussie imploring him to stop. I think this event made redundant all his coming attempts at courtship. I even took her side and said, "If someone wants to stop, then you should stop."

No matter. With the inherent despotism of a schoolteacher and a German one at that, he struck another blow for tyranny. I repeat: Irmin Opper was an uncoopperative.....person.

If you're still reading about my summer vacation, as one would imagine you must be, you deserve to know why am I so down on this Australian woman whose name I have forgotten (would that my entire recollection of her had followed). So here it is: she regularly complained that we never took her suggestions, what she wanted to do; the irony of that being Borogoi was the last thing she wanted to do. Her suggestions unfailingly were *not* to do something Irmin or I wished to do. Not one positive thought came exploding out of her head after Borogoi. Since she only opposed ideas, when we went ahead with them over her objection, to her we had not done what she wanted to do. Suited to a funeral procession more than a grand adventure, her unceasing attempt to throw a wet blanket on the most exciting, funnest thing I ever did made me resent her presence in it.

Compounding this was the misery of riding in the back even if it was only 1/3 the time. With new math, 1/3 was five times as long as 2/3. So I was mad at myself for letting her come and took it out on her I suppose; made worse by her inability to get to the bank or something and couldn't pay in full up front, posing the prospect that all the discomfort absolutely was for naught.

Well, I certainly feel better now.

The rains had just begun so we had some invigorating times getting our vehicle from Mud A to Mud B. We encountered two major bogs, the first already holding fast a Land Rover. Locals were hovering about the site like prehistoric buzzards over a tar pit and they recommended we take the left side of the road. Apparently the Land Rover driver had agreed with the locals, who were gainfully employed in excavating his conveyance. My passengers, who knew remarkably little about driving, as they did all else it seemed, were likewise convinced that was the best avenue. I pointed out the glaringly obvious fallacy in their reasoning and overruled them, as was my prerogative being the renter of the car *and* the only one in it with half a brain.

A solid bank to the right of the mud would require driving on a forty-five degree angle at first. The plan got little traction with my partners but there we were, Irmin Opper preparing for the most exciting driving of his life, me trapezing off the right side for balance. Yahoo it worked, to the chagrin, I imagine, of the Land Rover operator who might have hoped for some vindication.

After the car leveled off, I dropped off and ran ahead scouting the terrain. So rapt was Irmin with our initial success that he passed me and drove into a stream where Suzuki rested nicely on her frame and the exhaust playing *I'm Forever Blowing Bubbles.* To panic and kill ignition at that point would likely destroy the engine by sucking water into it. As long as the exhaust keeps blowing out, Irmin, there's no problem. Irmin came through like a champ. The car was so light we lifted her rear end and pushed her out, sputtering and indignant and ready to carry on.

With the Aussie up front I was driving blissfully along, not a care in the world. I've never understood how we didn't see that gale-whipped sea of mud coming. As it was, it arrived as a tremendous shock. We surfed rather than drove through the improbable morass, waves of mud often cresting above the windows, me trying to keep the gears meshed with my left hand (right hand drive like England), right hand flinging the wheel this way and that, and then this way again, my entire being focused on keeping the tires on the highest mud in front of us and keeping the trenches between the wheels. This from only a moment before, Sunday- driving along with not a job in the world beyond looking for bogs. We were so far into it that if we got stuck, it seemed we may not get out. None in the ship expected to emerge from the other side of the hurricane. On reaching a plateau where I could stop and shift into four-wheel drive for the home stretch, we felt the recipients of an automotive mud miracle.

Said Irmin Opper in his German sort of way, "I'm only glad I wasn't driving when we hit that." So was I.

Spilling over with awe and admiration the Aussie said, "You're really quite a good driver, aren't you?"

For that I immediately conferred upon her recognition for the understatement of the year. When beholding excellence, I acknowledge it.

This day we would see many groups of beautiful striped horses standing in the rain or in the spaces between showers.

Planning the trip included getting fuel in the next and final town, Maralal. Without refilling our jerry cans there, we would not have enough gas.

That the theme of honest narration might continue to prevail, the author admits he may have gotten a little carried away with his description of a muddy road, gale-whipped sea of mud and all; waves cresting higher than the windows. But even such hyperbole fights in the cause of accuracy as it is less important to describe how it was as to convey how it seemed to the author and his partners. Thus he is better able to put the reader in the moment. This is what he is striving for. Let me also state that if the reader should encounter hyperbole in the coming pages not followed by a disclaimer, then it is not hyperbole at all but the true facts.

Arriving in Maralal we received a mud pie in the face: we were told there was no gas. I found this disturbing but not catastrophic, never doubting that, having come that far, I would reach the Jade Sea. At this point our agendas diverged.

Spokesman for The Living Dead, the German said, "We must go back."

The reader probably suspects I had not endured morning tea torture, bogs and the constant company of my partners to build character; and he/she would be right. With what we'd overcome to get where we were, Irmin's words were astounding and more disturbing than the bad news. After recovering my faculties, I replied in a detached manner, "No, we're not going back. Maybe you're going back but I will reach that lake. I'll drive this thing until it runs out and then I'll panhandle gas from any vehicle that happens to come along. And I don't care how long it takes."

The German and the Aussie viewed with a solid dose of horror my resolve to continue: "What?!?" Irmin ejaculated, shirt rolling up, leather pants falling down and sauerkraut flying out his ears, "You cannot expect to go on. We must go back. There is no other way!"

"Irmin," I said, "Pull up your pants."

From that point on they festered with the terrible realization that they had cast their lot with that most dreaded of exotic perils, the Crazy American. And I was amazed at how easily daunted were my partners. They had had their adventure and were ready to go home now. Irmin and the Aussie were worried and I was disgusted.

Still I was not terribly bothered concerning my own plans because I was quite capable of stranding them in Maralal and proceeding on alone, liberated from riding in back. I could hardly have planned it better.

However, once again I displayed good old American can-do, turning the town upside down and dumping everybody out and this time finding the one and only man who could get us some gas. He promised to provide it the next day and he did, so the out-of-tune trio endured. Though we gladly would have paid an outrageous price, he charged barely over the Nairobi rate. This was the first of many times I would observe what seemed an absence of greed in the character of East Africans.

In the morning the Aussie graced us with her absence and after gassing up we waited an hour for her. This waiting was Irmin the Opperator's idea. I hated to squander a Heaven-sent opportunity to improve our gas mileage. We could pick her up on the way back. Finally my nearly limitless supply of patience was depleted and we were getting in the car to leave when the nightmare recurred. She had been stubbornly seeking bread, which did not exist in Maralal. When I chastised her for wasting our time, she cut me to the quick. She looked right at me and said, "You are not a real traveler because no real traveler would be without bread."

After recoiling from this broadside, I'm pretty sure I insulted her back but not strongly enough to make her stay in town. Probably I said something like, "If you say it, you're it." It was her lack of faith in my angling skills that bugged me the most. I had assured them we'd be knee deep in fish directly we reached the lake. That was good enough for me.

So – back on the road again, we had seen each others' true colors. They were unspeakably lame and I was a madman.

In a spirit of fairness toward Irmin, I note here that in general Americans seem to have it all over Europeans for spirit of adventure. This is their perception also considering the many times Europeans have told me, "You're such an American." I always take it as a compliment. I think how you take a comment is all that's important anyway. This is what they call granting the benefit of the trout.

Although we alternated one hour shifts in the back, it seemed I always was there, scrunched up, banging my head on the roof as we bounced along and unable to view the scenery adequately. All this suffering for a boring person who probably wasn't going to pay her way. I tell you it was irritating. As the tallest and most scrunched, I watched the time and made sure I didn't exceed my term by a second. The Aussie didn't drive. Looking back, it had been far too decent of me to include myself in the back sharing. Just too damn decent. Must come from eating 3 Musketeers in a democracy.

If a smooth stretch of track, Irmin would drive along enraptured by himself and the adventure he was on, quite unwilling to surrender the wheel. At times I thought I could hear *The Ride of the Valkyries* leaking out his ears as he skillfully steered us toward our goal.

He felt I should be slipshod with my timekeeping. One time demanding release from the back, I must have wrecked the Wagnerian fantasy prancing about in his head. “If you keep acting like this,” he cried, “you will spoil the trip for us all.”

In spite of personality conflicts we continued amicably, the experience we shared bigger than petty squabbles. On and on we penetrated a broader expanse than I could have imagined. Distance, distance and more distance spreading out from us in every direction; distance seemed the only real thing, all else window dressing in the face of it – the assertion of desert, huge boulders, a few nearby acacia trees flitting by and to our left a mountain range incomprehensibly far away, floating out there disconnected from the horizon like a mirage. We investigated an abandoned Masai mud hut and abandoned weaverbird nests hanging by the dozens from a short tree and wondered why everything was abandoned. Nearby a small, shallow pond was not abandoned, its surface thoroughly dotted with turtle heads. I made a few casts for fish with no luck and wondered what in the world the turtles lived on.

We reached a village called Tum but gave it the Borogoi treatment, not because Irmin was driving but the uninviting presence of heavily armed Africans loitering there.

Off careening through the uninhabited desert again, me marveling at how I had come to be there bearing down on this lake unknown to me, I thought, until recently. I imagined that moment when the Jade Sea would appear before us in all its improbability. The track was solid and we were making good time. We were a moving point in a near infinity. We spotted ahead of us and far to the right three separate black dots moving together toward the track. We waited for them. The dots stretched out and we saw it was two girls and a smaller boy. And then they were standing before us. The girls looked really fantastic, festooned with all manner of baubles and things. The girls were friendly and they posed for my partners who had a real photo session while the boy grimaced and gestured menacingly. Irmin gushed, “Everyone will say to me, 'where have you been?!?'” I stood back and took a few candid shots. I value those photos now but if my fellow tourists had not initiated it, taking pictures would not have occurred to me.

Down the road farther we met a small group of robust Masai morans (young men of warrior age) out for a stroll. Each was clad in goat skin and carried a staff. We stopped and greeted them also. They were cheerful and laughing about something, I suspected it concerned their own scanty attire in front of us. They seemed to take us in stride, just one more crazy thing in a crazy world.

I heard of Masai, though largely pastoral people, sometimes wiping out a tourist safari on the occasion of a tribal tenet willfully violated. Later Mr. Opper would push us toward such an occasion.

More sheer delight flying through this desolate and wild terrain. The track had been for some time distinct and pretty decent, more evidence that all good things come to an end.

When the road had deteriorated to nothing distinguishable from the rest of the sandscape and I was driving at about one mile per hour (it was Irmin's turn but, oddly, he had lost his taste for it) rolling over boulders in what vaguely resembled a dry stream bed and I remained convinced our heading was correct because I couldn't recall any tempting alternatives and seeing my passengers needed reassuring, I said so. I said, "Yes – see – there are mountains to our left. Just as the map says there ought to be."

Finally flowing over with despair, Irmin Opper wrenched from his persecuted heart and set forth upon the world the wild German moan, "This is never the road." Over and over again as if showing off his ability to turn a phrase in English. For years Mom got mileage out of that, pulling it out whenever we got a little lost.

The character of our path morphed from boulders to a flat generic expanse of sand as if we had been dropped into the middle of a desert. Having exhausted his opinion, Irmin quietly found solace in the post-hummus admiration he would reap from his countrymen as they read with grief and pride the headline **GERMAN ADVENTURER DISAPPEARS**. He conjures a beautiful young woman, not German. She is Italian, carrying in her armpit a newspaper proclaiming the shocking story of a man pulled by the Stone Age from the apex of civilization.

This image of Aryan desire has emerged from a record store amid a crowd of customers. If we might look also, we see that all have bought the same album: *Irmin Opper's Favorite Oppera,* subtitled Tannhauser. We follow the glowing beauty as she pursues the streets of Rome to her palatial home.

She enters her bedroom, firmly closing the door behind her, graceful fingers lingering on the knob, then reluctantly falling from it like a screaming greased pig from a precipice. Tears welling in her dark eyes, she places the newspaper on a chair as delicately as it were a magazine. Then with undeniable longing the swarthy princess dumps the record from its jacket and as gently as Anna Karenina would present herself to the wheels of an approaching juggernaut, she lays it on the turntable. The lovely mourner lifts the stylus from its cradle like it was a baby German.

We cannot with decency look any longer upon this anemic scene of love lost. But Irmin can. Through clouded eyes he sees her desperately searching the disc for the band which will render *Evening Star,* her nickname for him. A trembling hand fails, dropping the needle loudly on this vinyl remnant of Irmin. She drops also, like a load of boiled noodles, onto the floor.

Sorry for Herr Opper his fantasy would not be realized on this day. As I was pursuing our course to certain doom, before us appeared a most unlikely little sign stuck in the sand. It read “South Horr,” not an advertisement but the name of the village we were struggling toward. My partners wouldn't have been more shocked seeing that while traveling through outer space. Through all the suspense the Aussie was silent. At least that's how I remember it.

The outskirts of South Horr was a startling and welcome contrast to the harshness we'd traversed, the dirt road to the mission lined with papaya and stately shade trees. Naturally this was the patch Whitey had staked out. We pulled in and met the priest. He told us many people were being killed around there. A fellow priest from his home village in Italy had been decommissioned within the year, returning from Tum. In the past three years, he said, a thousand villagers had been terminated. The responsible parties fell into three categories: soldiers of Idi Amin hiding out in the mountains until they get hungry for cattle; Turkana tribesmen gone wild after breaking into a munitions dump of the recently dumped Amin; and raiding Ethiopian Shifka. As we spoke, a message came over the wireless that three-hundred of these fellows were making their way through the hills toward us.

The priest told us the area had been abundant with elephants but the wife of Kenya's first president, Jomo Kenyatta, had them killed off for the ivory. Having not yet mastered the superior African way of speaking, he opined, “She was a real bitch.”

In this village we met natives selling bags of aqua marines and garnets. In the evening the village chorus practiced in the church. I'd never heard anything like it. Maybe just a coincidence but it seemed like what angels should sound like singing. Or, I suppose, farting. When the leader spied me listening from the door, he invited me to join. Much as I would love to be part of something like that, it would be like mixing sand into an angel food cake so I declined.

We passed a restless night in the mission yard, a space the priest dubbed not yet violated, Irmin drinking from his treasured coconut shell bowl, souvenir of Lamu Island. This murdering was something of interest to Irmin after all and we slept fitfully that night, far from Suzuki on advice of the priest, in case she should be desired by someone.

In the morning we felt our bodies for holes and got on our way early, without tea; then I knew they didn't need the stuff. They drank it only to rile me; and make me paranoid.

By skipping tea, we hoped to beat the invading horde to the point where they would reach the road so that, proceeding from there, we would miss them. Admittedly this makes us look like typical snobby tourists who don't enjoy mingling with the locals. In our defense, I feared they would engage us in meaningless chit-chat and quite frankly, we didn't have the time or the Swahili for it.

As we drove along, Irmin blurted in alarm that in his haste he had left behind the bowl. Deepening the rift between him and the malcontented object of his desire, she said she had noticed it as we were leaving. He angrily railed, “Why didn't you pick it up?”

“It wasn't mine to pick up,” she replied in the true spirit of “every man for herself.” This reason Irmin did not find satisfactory. I suppose he had fantasized drinking from it in Germany as the emblem of his African experience.

“You can get another one, Irmin,” I counseled him kindly, “in Germany. It'll look just like that one. After a while you'll think it is the other one.”

“No, it's not the same,” Irmin replied, heartbroken. Then I knew he and that bowl must have had some times together. It wasn't only a matter of him recognizing his bowl, but the bowl knowing him.

I hope you have not heard the sound of a heartbroken German. The melancholy of it cannot be forgotten, or even washed from your clothes - like a lowing cow. It makes ordinary German despair sound like yodeling.

"No really," I soothed, "you can get your beer in it and Germans will still say, 'Hey Opper, why do you always drink from that ugly brown bowl?' and then you can tell them it's the skull of your pet monkey in Africa."

But he was inconsolable.

After South Horr no human settlements remained between us and our goal. More bouncing and zooming along through the desert with one person (not me) crashing around on top of the packs, trying to snatch a look out the window while not breaking anything. The track was very good here including an inexplicable fifty yards of pavement, like aliens put it down for their flying saucer. More roaring along through this astounding world. We were drawing near and I knew my first sight of this lake would be one of the great moments of my life. I was looking for it around every bend – beyond every hill, straining with anticipation as we topped every rise. Suddenly – there it was before us in all its savage beauty - The Jade Sea. Not green, it was a deep blue that the hot, dusty cliffs and desert sands could not blot up. It looked not like a long-lost section of Nile but like a very long-lost piece of the Gulf Stream.

We drove to water's edge where I spied the promising sign of small fish bones on the shore. I cast a Limper and retrieved it. The water was not clear but as the lure neared I could see fish following and taking swipes at it. Though pleased, I was not surprised. Fifteen minutes after reaching Lake Turkana, we had a small pile of Nile tilapia, tiger fish and vindication for lunch and all were delighted with the bounty.

After eating we cruised up the most driveable stretch we had seen in some time, a little above the lake. I looked down and saw a large Nile crocodile sunning on the shore, the first croc I'd ever seen excepting Ol' Bonecrusher at Gatorland. Then we were paralleling the water for some time but had lost sight of it as the road had turned away. I had not come that far to lose sight of the lake, thinking, "Oh well. It's over there somewhere." Fortunately I was driving so no need to convince Mr. UncoOpperative about the next move. I threw her into four-wheel drive and turned left to head cross-desert in what I felt was the direction of the lake. I shudder now to think of my life deprived of that one simple turn of a steering wheel.

The poor optimistic fools had underestimated my perversity, never imagining we wouldn't stay on track like a train and go directly to the first village, Lloyangalani. They had little chance to object as immediately I was occupied trying to keep us moving and no turning back now. No, no, no turning back. Ride 'em cowgirl. Yeeha! I had been sure we could cross anything in that little recurring miracle but a couple ancient streambeds had a quicksand-like quality that was surprising and tried to suck us down.

The reward far outstripped the risk. After twenty minutes of terror, driving with my fingers crossed, my upended passengers arrived where I don't think even Masai or Turkana had visited in a long time. My reasoning is this: If you saw gold bars lying around you'd suspect a place lightly visited by the civilized. Firewood in this region, we would learn, is esteemed more than gold and scarcer. The spot where we found the lake again was covered with the stuff.

Never could I have imagined that such a wonderful place existed, much less that I would be there. Pigs in poop had nothing on me. As I blissfully surveyed our Stone Age surroundings, about as pleased as I could be with life, white pelicans skimmed by with their best pterodactyl imitation, wing tips skating on the frothing chop.

Adam and Eve were off discussing something. Soon they approached and in carefully couched terms orchestrated to seduce me Adam said with his quaint original accent, "This has been a nice place to visit but hadn't we better get going now so that we can reach Lloyangalani and find lodging for the night?"

The lodging monster once again rearing its ugly head. You could have knocked me over with an ant fart. I mean it. That's all it would have taken to lay me out. Just catch an ant fart and fling it at me. I'm done. Luckily no ants around. I looked at them and sincerely thought, "Why are you even alive?"

Were they really that unappreciative? I ask you, the reader. Is my surprise unwarranted? I mean, should I have clairvoyantly seen this coming? Hey. Wait a minute. You wouldn't be siding with those lameos. Come on. Really? Oh, just kidding? That's good, because I was about to activate the lion fart embedded in your book. Yes, technology has come that far.

Like Jimmy Buffett, it could be my fault. Having not yet fully comprehended my partners, I had assumed them excited as I was about this marvelous spot I had taken the trouble to arrive them at. Once assured they weren't pulling my leg, I began regarding them as something as worthy of my attention as trigonometry. Keeping it simple, I said, "This is what I came here for. If you want to leave, you're welcome to take the Suzuki and go but as for me, I'm going fishing." And I grabbed my rod and some lures and exited stage left. Irmin frequently sided with Aussie to gain her favor which he was eternally after, among other things. For all I know, in his heart he wanted to stay. Soon I would experience some memorable fishing.

I found a likely looking spot where a minute flow seemed to start in the sand, and trickle a few yards into the lake. By casting straight out and allowing my Limper to sink to the bottom, nearly every time I caught a large tilapia and the occasional tiger fish. I buried a four-pound tilapia in wet, dark sand and walked the shore to the left, casting. Next to shore I hooked something much bigger and different. To my lifelong frustration, it got off. Perhaps it was the famed Nile perch, of which giant specimens are known to lurk in Lake Turkana. An hour after burying the tilapia, I returned and dug it up, still as lively as when I had caught it, although surely wondering what this new phase in life was about.

When I got back, the First Couple still were marking the spot. At the time I thought it must have been out of choice but reflecting on it, probably they didn't trust themselves to get the vehicle back to the track.

They never believed I had caught anything but the fish I returned with and they viewed that with disbelief. It was the largest fish they'd ever seen. I don't think Irmin even believed I caught that one: "You caught that fish with that little rod?!?"

"What do you think I did," I said, "buy it at a fish house around the corner?"

Irmin took photos of me cooking it on my fire of sticks and it felt like I had shifted from tourist to native. They dined on it thanklessly with me, though very happy to have it. That was the best freshwater fish I ever ate, setting notwithstanding.

The Australian Ambassador retired to the vehicle and I rinsed my clothes in the lake. Even the jeans were dried in twenty minutes by the hot wind blasting through them. While my pants danced without me off the end of a driftwood log, I went for a swim. Finally reconciled to his fate, Irmin joined me. This was a third degree experience for him and transformative. It was Irmin Opper who stepped gingerly into the whitecaps but with my own two eyes I saw Siegfried emerge. Sun dropping behind him, powerful, potent wind thrashing the lake about his knees and throwing his long, curly locks about; Lake Turkana cascading from his thick, blonde mustache, the lean Aryan hero strode naked from the Jade Sea. Brandishing a driftwood sword he slew the invisible mob of Turkana barring him from the refuge of shore, displaying a warrior I should have guessed earlier when Irmin confided, "My greatest fear is to die without defense."

For this night he would be spared on both counts.

Flush with victory, Siegfried stood with me like Adam and Adam. Buffeted by stupendous wind, the only men on Earth dripped while flamingos flew before an astounding fan of blue and orange beams that banished Sun from that barren cradle of mankind and invited the rest. The universe opened overhead like a supermarket, featuring brilliant lights in a three dimensional black infinity I never had suspected. The lee shore of the wild desert sea stretched to the edge of it and the wind began pouring from outer space itself. We watched a gibbous moon rise from the jiggling water and pin itself on the cosmos and my happiness was complete.

Call it the windward side of time if you like, but we had strayed from the influence of humanity farther than I thought possible, like it hadn't started yet, leaving Michaelangelo's Davy Crockett, Jesus and grief still to be born; no tribalism, bigotry or wars plagued us, no Plague, Plato or opinions, no Good & Plenty or plenty o' nothin'; no rummies, mummies or Piltdown Woman's suffrage, no South Africa, televisions or Joan of Arkansas - no leaders, love, losers or Lohengrin to name a few – no s.o.b.'s - all having percolated from the future, through now, into a fairy tale called history, of no relevance for us. Which begs the question of what we were then.

Irmin lamented, “No one will understand when I try to tell them about this.”

Finally something he and I could agree upon. Describe all I want, it's only an exercise in how near I can miss remembering. The reader will glean from the effort that *something* worth relating was happening. For what it was, she must look inward or take himself there.

Later on the Aussie entreated me to set up my pup tent, which even Siegfried knew would be impossible in that wind. The old Irmin kicked Siegfried back into the lake and chimed in with his femme fatale. Me, I love sleeping in the wind, perhaps a legacy of Florida where it is the only antidote for mosquitoes. I gave in and made the attempt so they'd shut up about it. As soon as the tent was out its bag, the wind flew in the door and blew it out like a bull in a candy store. In an instant my tent had become a flying tiger fish on a long tail. It was all we could do to knock it down, deflate it and put the thing away. She was convinced and returned to the mechanized shelter.

Irmin and I sat up on the lee side of what he spoke of as “the fire to keep lions away,” letting the wind pin our bedding to our backs. The fire was an effective ploy, also deterring tigers, rabid polar bears, tax collectors, Ed McMahon and other untold enemies. Irmin's blankets kept blowing off and when the fire went out, the libertine excused himself and joined the vehicular woman, leaving me to fend off the lions as best I could. The only four footed animal we saw there was a little jackal that cruised through on its way to Ethiopia.

Next morning we followed our tracks back to the track and motored on to the village Lloyangalani so we could have chapatis. Very important. Watching my companions one would guess this the sole reason for leaving Nairobi. Maybe for them until you've eaten chapatis, you haven't been to a place. Tea there which they called tchai as in short for tchaikovsky, had a delightful distinctive flavor but I could not discover the mystery ingredient. The people who might have known didn't speak English.

By the lake we met Sudanese net fishermen whose three-day butterflied catch of tilapia spread across the stony lifeless ground dessicating in the solar breath as if they'd been caught on an uninhabitable planet. Ninety-three million miles those particular rays traveled just to dry those fish. That's what I call service. They were very interested when I told them of my fishing spot.

After setting out the nets, they took Irmin and me for a paddle in their big extravagant dugout that had an actual fountain in front. One man bailed constantly to ensure water beneath us enough to maintain the display. It was an impressive lot of work for an aesthetic effect. Likely they'd have happily dispensed with the fountain if they could have plugged the hole but the fishing was great because they had paddled to a place where folks had no need of hole plugging materials.

They used concave curved paddles that dig efficiently into the water. I had done some canoeing in my day though never with so excellent a paddle, and they were surprised and delighted to see I could use it. I wondered at their reaction. Perhaps assuming a visitor would be unfamiliar with a device as primitive as a paddle, they were glad there wasn't so much distance between us after all. Irmin declined trying but busted his buttons over my proficiency. I suppose where he failed to glorify Germany, at least I upheld the white race.

The man bailing had a fever and he took a dip out the canoe to cool off as did I though I had no fever yet. They advised us to choose our swimming spots wisely. In other words "don't feed the crocodiles."

Strangely enough crocs see us as an antidote for hunger and nothing more, considering not our self importance. We are important to them only in the aggregate.

The sick man hailed from a tribe different from his friends and he looked different. I wondered if he had been a soldier. He was milk chocolate, stocky and muscular and wore old camo while his pals were slender and black and shiny as ebony.

When we returned to shore the fountain automatically quit and the fishermen stepped out and hauled their net. An unlucky catfish wiggled in it. Catfish are the one fish that seems to live everywhere. You wonder if their perfect design spontaneously generated them around the globe or if they spread from a single point of origin, the abominable tryst of a cat and a fish. While pondering this, a thought near took my breath away. What if Lake Turkana is not only the cradle of mankind but catfish as well?? This would explain why we have marched together through time, exemplified by luminaries like Jim "Catfish" Hunter, Nelson "Catfish" Mandella and Nancy "Catfish" Pelosi.

They cooked the enigma for us while we enjoyed music from a gas-can guitar made and played by the brown man. People will find a way to have music. I gave them some kidogo (small) money for this experience but the leader, Swalik Ratabu, said to me,

"Never again. After this we are friends."

They were a gentle bunch of young men, reclining with their impossibly white smiles in their lean-to shelter from the sun like a pile of puppy dogs and holding each others' hands. I can tell when a place suits me and this was as far as I needed Suzuki to go. Had I the foresight to bring a decent pack and/or Mr. Munich hadn't lost half my lures while I was trying to let him catch a fish, I'd have bade my partners happy adieu so I could explore this marvel at my leisure. I would have walked around the southern end of the lake, arrived one day at our campsite of the previous night, gone on and some day showed up at the village on the western shore. Assuming a crocodile didn't catch me at some point, what a stroll that would have been.

When Irmin and I were out boating, the Aussie perched on a rock tanning her teats. They still were out when we got back in and by thunder, they were pretty damn good teats. As Tonto would say, "Mmm. Plenty good." I don't blame her for being proud and I'm sure they inflamed Irmin to the breaking point. Those who think I am prejudiced against the girl see now that I report things as I find them. In fact I gave her the benefit of the doubt in this, sparing her display close inspection for my own sake as well as hers. I like to be able to think there is something good about everybody.

It was incongruous though, like cactus flowers.

We were checking out Lloyangalani when precocious ten-year old Turkana Agostino Lowoi, presaging his future, strode up and furnished us a trajectory. The mission school term had ended and in pretty good English he asked to be returned to his village. I checked with the missionary and he approved so on we went and at last I had a pal.

In an earlier time Agostino and his mother had crossed the mountains to the lake. We brought him to his adoptive village, riding in the back with Aussie. It was a fun ride all the way. I suggested we sing a song and rendered a stirring first verse of

Swing Low Sweet Chariot. I asked master Lowoi if he knew it. He replied simply "No," so I gave up the idea. About a minute later I heard from the back a little voice singing, "I looked up yonder and what did I see, comin' for to carry me home, a band of angels watching over me, comin' for to carry me home."

Oddly enough the melody was not unlike Swing Low Sweet Chariot and it carried that distinct intonation imparted to a song sung through a sly grin.

East African snails give escargot a bad name by imparting a nasty disease that enters through your toes, prevalent in the shallows of most lakes, preventing bathing from the shore.

Haiku to Bilhartzia

Damn snails

Serendipity at its best, Turkana turned out to be free of it. Probably that was too much desert for the first snail to drag its belly across. Or any snail for that matter. One must wonder how close the intrepid snails of legend came to introducing the disease. Consider the tragic hero Slopeye the Snailorman covered in olive oil, portaging his whimsical craft only to tragically dry up in sight of the lake; being invertebrate, his tiny corncob pipe all that remained to tell the tale.

He's Slopeye the Snailorman
Set out on a frying pan
All covered with oil
So he'd never broil
Was Slopeye the Snailorman
Boop! boop!

And there we have it. Luckily Lake Turkana wasn't the Cradle of Mankind, Catfish and Snails. So the boy and I went down to the shore and swam and splashed and played while the Aussie found another rock to further tan her teats off of.

Caught up in the gaiety of the moment, Irmin joined us in all the glory he could muster. Far out on the lake schools of tiger fish much bigger than the ones I had caught, could be seen slashing schools of smaller fish. I waited until Irmin had swum pretty far out and then shouted a warning about the tiger fish, named in part for their menacing, protruding teeth. We watched him race in with remarkable speed considering his style. Curious, I later asked if it was a point of honor with Germans to swim using only one hand when escaping danger but he did not give an answer that I feel I can trust. Then Agostino and I were racing on the beach and as we ran I noticed I felt a little less strong.

With my camera Irmin photographed Agostino seated atop my shoulders. Then, as if Agostino were a prop, he said, "I too would like such a picture with Agostino," So the boy briefly swapped rides and entered a German slide show.

The village of Agostino was round thatched huts situated near the lake; no windows, no garden. The thatch must be imported. I wonder if the Mars Rover would find signs of life on Earth's baked volcanic surface here. It is locally owned and you can make a hut anywhere you like. After it's completed, you pay the community for the spot it's on.

So far Irmin had avoided shaking hands but here the disaster was forced upon him. From this I learned a valuable lesson in African traveling. We had finished shaking hands with some of the villagers and the danger was subsiding, so Irmin produced his trusty bottle of alcohol with which, in front of God and everybody else, he doused his hands. Then the generous fellow insisted I do it. I suppose his purification would be nullified if I carried all the diseases to the car.

Ever after that I had my own bottle equipped with aerosol so I could take the precaution one step further. When I sensed that some impulsive savage was bound to shake, I would spray alcohol on his hand before it intercepted mine. After the catastrophic greeting I doused mine as Irmin had taught me. They always thought it was holy water or something and were very happy about it.

I do wonder if Irmin employs this safeguard in his homeland and if not, if it's the people here that inspire it or the location. After touching a Negro in Germ-many, I wonder if he would cleanse himself. I'm pretty sure he would feel the impulse.

We set ourselves up a little ways from the village. Although she had not seen him for two months, Agostino's mother seemed pretty blasé' about his return but she did greatly appreciate some powdered soup from the Aussie. She and Irmin went to the village and returned very pleased because they'd been inside a hut. I wasn't the least interested in going inside a hut but it was something they had done on their own and they felt good about it. "We've been inside a hut," she announced to me. I was surprised Irmin would risk it with no way to get sandblasted immediately on exiting. Maybe he anointed himself while inside.

I despaired of our ability to cook supper for there was insufficient firewood; indeed in my opinion there was none at all and I wished we had transferred some from our previous camp. Agostino to the rescue - at ten the most self sufficient person I knew. He showed us how to cook on three finger size sticks not one but three pots of soup.

That day Agostino had found me a gift, a jawbone of a Nile perch, pronounced there as one word with the accent on the first syllable. This bone is an excellent spoon, as I learned that night. It is smooth and imparts to the meal its own good flavor.

It was another magical night. I had to keep pinching myself as we sat by our Lilliputian fire cooking soup, watching the three-quarters moon bouncing around in the lake shallows. By contrast, when the lunar orb forsook the cosmos to play in the water, the bright white marker remained almost still for the time when the moon must return, content and full of moisture to rain somewhere else. (If you didn't notice what a terrific metaphor that was, the author suggests you give it another try.)

As spare as their habitat, the tall, thin men of the village, returning from a meeting off in the scrub, squatted one at a time briefly at our fire and greeted Agostino. They invited Irmin and me to a ceremony planned for the next day.

Irmin generally was an affable, humorous sort, kind of a good German but still an assh..., a German. Irmin the German – there you have it. As such he already had insulted with his Germaphobia the people we were visiting and he was about to show he did not respect their customs, which would place us on the brink of calamity. It was like Irmin never grasped that the people here were real and should be respected; and, like people anywhere, could be provoked.

In the morning I scaled a cliff to watch the sun peak out from its burrow under the desert. From my perch I also had an overview of the village. The huts mostly sat on a peninsula jutting into the lake with a circular goat corral set off a small way from the beach and the village. I saw the men filing away and into the scrub.

A common denominator for people everywhere, it's always men getting up to silly enterprises and who attach to them grave importance. If it's not some ritual ceremony then it's a Kiwanis Club meeting; and then, of course, war. Meanwhile women are carrying on a routine and doing what's necessary. So – men are much more interesting than women.

I returned to ground level and we drove to the clearing of interest. On arriving we saw scattered groups each comprised of a couple of (what else?) men, a fourteen year old boy and an unhappy goat. Able to see the future, goats would have been unhappier still; unless this damnable incarnation was sufficient to urge them passed it. For a touch of variety at this inclusive showing, also present were the priest from the Lloyangalani mission with his Super 8 camera, two white-robed nuns standing side by side like a set of bleached penguins and an unidentified

Caucasian male. The nuns were a surprise as we had been told no women could attend. Maybe they qualified for an exemption.

We could have bought the right to photograph the event with a kidogo payment, maybe one shilling but I was feeling too sorry for the goats to care about it. Irmin was too cheap and didn't want to "spoil" the natives as he was always saying (spoiling being a process whereby they would lose their native charm by getting paid for value given, like Europeans).

The tribesmen did a bit of dancing with their spears, not an unrealistic substitute for the women. And then they fell to their true purpose, which was not Bingo and not a group therapy session. It was the slitting of the living goats' throats from south to north so the boys could insert their head in the cavity and slurp all the hot blood. And what a lot of slurping was going on. Whole lot of slurping. I wondered if Agostino would have his day with this.

Suddenly, angry, animated Turkana stood in front of Irmin and me, not facing forward to protect us from an advancing enemy, no, spears cocked and indicating us. (I can now say with authority that if you want to get a point across, forget about your laser pointer. Spear- cocked is the way to go.)

That was when I learned that, characteristically disregarding our hosts and failing to consult me, Irmin had attempted double suicide by recording the scene at belt level with his little spy-camera. After watching *The Naked Prey*, I vowed always to avoid this situation, but here I am anyway. It's enough to make you afraid to get out of bed. Now do I get roasted, faced off with a cobra or run down and speared?

The daring cheapskate had been caught by these folks who recognize not only a camera when they see it but subterfuge and ingratitude as well. I felt discriminated against, thinking it unfair to threaten me as if I were German too. The scene was tense with Irmin trying to profess some kind of ignorance. I recall little aversion to offering him up in appeasement, roasting probably the way to go. We got off with severe reprimands and payment which included the camera. Later on the priest informed us about what we could have had.

It is my impression from this and instances to come that East Africans have no tolerance for deceit and life commonly is the price exacted for it. It's a solid way to keep honesty uppermost in the gene pool. Perhaps we got off lightly because we were no threat to that.

Fish roam the eastern shore of Lake Turkana with relative impunity, the people subsisting mainly on maize and whatever the goats give them and fruits from other villages. One village, of the Elmolo people, is known to catch and eat crocodiles. The priorities there can be seen clearly from a past Peace Corps initiative to teach the natives to fish. The Peace Corps brought them boats. When the Corps' work was done and they left, the newly educated Africans knew just what to do with that amazing windfall of firewood. Thirty-nine is about the maximum age allowed there by nature. I guess they've got no time for fishing.

People have told me I was fortunate to visit when I did because change was coming. Already a Scandinavian company was fishing the west side and flying the catch to Nairobi daily. The priest said the Turkana were allowing their ceremonies to be photographed because they believed their traditions doomed and they wished them preserved.

For citizens of industrial nations it seems the world is a time machine. We won't turn back the clock on our own turf to a more natural setting but darned if we can't find it somewhere else, right back to the tree people of Indonesia. And then we can picture Ben Franklin and gauge how far we've come. We assume of course, the other animals to be the same as they ever were, not evolving as a conglomerate – primitive then, primitive now, just plain primitive wherever they are. Nothing to look at there.

I intended, as I thought did my companions, to motor on up to the northeast shore and head east along the Ethiopian border as we had agreed in Nairobi. Once again resistance in spite of the

Lloyangalani priest's report that the road was in good shape. I don't recall if I mentioned the prospect of gold. This attitude drains one after awhile, like oil from the car; three adventurers with one adventurous spirit divided among them. An adventurous spirit divided cannot stand. The little thirds keep falling over.

I was dissuaded from the plan, buying the idea that Marsabit National Park could be a worthy alternative. I think I intended a trade-off but it was a bad bargain on my part. There was a failed attempt to dump the Aussie at the mission.

Our new route would take us northeast, away from the lake and then loop south to Nairobi, east of the route we had taken up. We did get far enough north that we began seeing camels and we stopped at a strange sort of wind-blown Arab outpost called North Horr. With only two Horrs in the area and widely separated, one supposes they did a lively trade. We had chapatis there in a mud cafe.

After that we were some time crossing a fascinating flat desert with mirages on all horizons, very real looking with true -to- life reflections. The mirages even appear in my slides. One can only imagine the torment of someone, say an Australian woman, stranded without water, crawling toward these oases that match her pace in retreat.

In a place that appeared incapable of supporting life, it was baffling to come upon groups of ostriches. I had great fun chasing them with the car, around and around, the birds kicking up dust a little ahead, for some reason reminding me of can-can dancers. The reader may think the ostriches not well served by these shenanigans but they seemed genuinely enjoying it as much as I was. Then everybody wanted a turn so it was Irmin and even the woman, who wouldn't drive down the road but couldn't resist harassing some wildlife.

We encountered gazelles also and gave them the same treatment, whoever wasn't driving photographing them on the run. When we're not there they probably race each other. The ostriches and gazelles seemed so out of place they were like hallucinations. Maybe they have adapted to drink mirages. Wouldn't that be something.

From the genesis of the trip my companions had been saying the word "Marsabit" with something akin to religious awe. Eventually we reached Marsabit National Park. It was the least interesting part of the trip and for them an anticlimax, having looked forward to it so. There were lots of big trees that blocked the view. And no chapatis. We did spot a couple elephants at a stream and I exited the car and approached one close enough to get it to flare its big old ears which terrified those sitting in the car, who thought it would charge. Or for Irmin even scarier, charge money. So anyway, that was worthwhile.

In the nearby town of Isiolo Irmin and the Aussie became fascinated with bracelets for sale of copper and brass. Considering this a sign they might sell in Florida, I left a hundred dollars in Kenya Shillings with a teenage boy Baleisa Hambuli who agreed to gather as many as he could and send them to General Delivery in Nairobi. My companions declared me crazy for doing this but I saw no reason not to trust the lad.

The materials came from Zaire. Baleisa took us to see people forging them. One man did it on a fire of sticks in his hut, a small hammer his only tool. Another had his fire in a small cavity in the ground. A bracelet could be made fifteen minutes to a half hour.

Overall the road back beat the one up. It held no traps; but one long stretch was so badly corrugated that it couldn't be driven slower than fifty miles per hour. If we had to stop, the car practically shook apart. When we returned it, all the bolts and screws had to be tightened.

The most invigorating moment arrived in a blinding dust cloud from a truck ahead of us. Suddenly we were face to face with a big truck on our side of the road going very fast. We would have been little more than another bug on its grill. I swerved and missed juggernauting death but it was an opportunity for the female, whose life I had unavoidably saved, to ask if I were trying to kill her. “I wasn't,” I replied dryly, “but it's not a bad idea.”

I wasn't feeling well and spent the first three or four nights in Nairobi on a bed at the Iqbal, weak and feverish, where I had an unexpected visitor.

Writer's apology: the writer confesses that, as you must have suspected, he has taken some latitude with the actual circumstances of the foregoing endeavor and portrayed himself meaner than he really is. This was to forge a more captivating account wrought not only from scenery and adventure, but personal conflicts as well.

Sharpening knife on my toenail

Les Miserables

Three dots resolved

sunbathing tilapias

"Gas-Can Segovia and Swalik Ratabu"

Agostino hamming it up

El Molo village

tilapia on the rocks

Nairobi Revisited

I suppose most Americans alone and on the verge of death see Ronald Reagan descend and hover above them; or Bullwinkle; or a fairy godfather enters and rescinds the contract. Maybe who appears hinges on where you are.

Though not a private room, I was alone in it, being mid-day. I had risen and tried walking to a hospital somewhere but I didn't know where or even if, so I gave it up and trudged back. Weak and fevered and miserable I lay abed wondering what had struck me down like this but I figured it probably came from Gas-can Segovia.

I missed her entrance but then she was before me, a vision of licorice. The skinny bucktoothed Masai glided to my bed and sat down, placing a hand on my leg. My heart warmed to this simple kindness being shown me but her intentions soon became clear. {The author would like to take a moment to marvel at the unpredictability of life. Isn't it something? Just when things seem to be going badly for you, something completely unexpected might happen to take your mind off it. You never really know.}

When I failed to respond vigorously to my visitor's ministrations, she resorted to sign language, making a circle with the thumb and index finger of one hand and poking in and out of it the index finger of the other. Though untutored in signing, I got her drift. Rarely have I been so romanced. I might even say never. This coy display should have won me but conditions were not favorable and I had to shake my head and whimper "Hapana" in reply. A cockeyed optimist, she reached the only conclusion available to her – that I had misread her hologram. She made it for me a couple times more with the same disheartening result.

This adventurer was not easily discouraged once a plan had lodged in her head. She had an ace (of hearts) up her sleeve and when that card was played, it took all my power, which admittedly wasn't much, to resist her. Confident of victory she glided to the sink across the room, there pressing a finger to one nostril and jetting out the other a stream of lava that would have shamed Mauna Loa. Scout's honor, the eruption lasted a good two minutes. That's how quickly she filled the sink, if you want to know the rate of discharge. Where it could possibly be coming from beggared the imagination and where it would wind up certainly not to be contemplated. By the end, one would have thought her entire presence transformed into goo, the feet the last to go through. Instead, somehow undiminished, she turned and cast me a sly glance filled with foreboding.

With the ease of a woman aware she has made herself irresistible, she slunk back to my bedside and grabbed her prize (how she found out I go for gross women, I'll never know. Maybe it was a shot in the dark). I say she grabbed her prize. She grabbed at it. The thing she went for hadn't been so diminutive since I was learning to walk. If it could have retracted entirely inside and snuck out the back and caught the next flight to Orlando, it would have. Had the episode lasted a little longer, I feel sure I would have emerged from it a woman.

Still she wasn't against mounting a search which I fended off as best I could. At last my new playmate saw the light, canceled the courtship and dove for my pockets.

After all, she'd been willing to put out. Nobody could say she wasn't. My lack of cooperation shouldn't mean she doesn't get paid. For her willingness. Do I think her time isn't worth something?? Well then I really couldn't believe my luck - laying there sick, dying *and* robbed. Plus everything we'd meant to each other was a sham. It seemed like she had more hands than I had pockets but I marshaled my remaining vigor and repelled her forays into my change. For me it wasn't so much the money as the principal of the thing, whatever that was. My surprise visitor was angered by her failure to prosper but she left. We never spoke again.

Another time at the Iqbal I was lying on my bunk and a woman walked by and grabbed me in the same popular place, never slowing down, like she couldn't resist checking. Gave me a little idea what it's like being a water meter.

Already I was fearing I had brought too little film, film being unavailable in Kenya. With wonderful serendipity a bald German ran a camera shop. He resold film procured from tourists on their way out. He also was one of the few people outside Germany who could repair my '60's German-made Kodak slr which was having issues. One other delight of Nairobi was fresh passion fruit juice available at one shop. Best juice I ever had.

About the time I got over my latest malady, Terry returned from safari. We were relieved to see each other, preferring not to visit Uganda alone; as if we would be any less dead in each other's company.

For a further injection of perspective, if either I or Terry fail to get a wild hair and go to Africa, i.e., I'm at Steak 'n' Shake having a big time with my curly fries or in the driveway fixing my van (again) or he's shearing a sheep or worse, then there's no happy reunion in Nairobi and one of us has to start heading to Uganda alone.

I wonder if the one who stayed home would feel some vague sense of loss that day, like he's let somebody down somehow, missed an appointment somewhere.

How about you? Have you had days when you felt like that?

Like maybe you'd left a whole lot on the table? Now maybe we know why. How about summer of '81? Might be there was supposed to be three of us.

Phynal foto?

Uganda Ho!

Just before leaving for Africa I read a frightening National Geographic article that absolutely eliminated Uganda from my itinerary. Here is a quote from a doctor trying to bring medical supplies into the country: *"We chased the setting sun toward Kampala with growing fear that the darkness would catch us still out in the countryside, prey to the human wolves called Kondos*[*]*...*

The elation that had swept the country after Amin's fall had by now, just four months later, done a complete turnabout. 'It's even worse than under Amin,' people told us ...

Darkness was upon us as we raced the last kilometers toward the haven of St.Nicholas' Greek Orthodox Church in Kasubi, a Kampala suburb. At one point two shots rang out only a few yards away. Engine backfiring, we swerved wildly around a corner. Now a small car cut ahead of us as a dark van pulled up behind. Men got out of both. Was this a hit?...

...Ten, twenty, thirty people a night were being killed in and around Kampala, many simply dragged from their homes and shot. Such justice had been handed out by Amin's hated secret police. But now the killing was anonymous – somehow even more terrifying ... as we plunged into this world of chaos."

Well, what's the point in being a Negative Nelly? Positive Polly had heard coffee could be bought ridiculously cheap in Uganda and mailed home equally cheap and that she could call

---

[*] In Florida it's the human wolves that *build* the condos.

home for next to nothing. Back in the United States of Addiction, such coffee would be easy to sell.

Certainly I had planned to forego the human wolves but that was when I thought I'd have the luxury. Hitchhiking counter-clockwise around Lake Victoria to reach Tanzania meant traversing the dreaded country..... mid- August and hitching through Kenya was turning out great. Our first night was in the town of Navaisha. Next morning we walked to the outskirts of town and got a ride with a friendly businessman from Nairobi. He took us all the way to the town past Nakuru. You know. That town.

I had hardly time to get two Fantas when Terry had flagged down a small pickup truck which took us to some village. There I ensured us a ride by trying to eat a sandwich, a trick I learned in Europe. It was a Hare Krishna of all things in a huge van. He brought us all the way to Kisumu on Lake Victoria. We got there about 1:30 and besieged the local Sikh temple.

Sikhs were known for putting up travelers for free but we also heard they were getting jaded by folks taking advantage of their hospitality and some temples were changing policy. We applied at this one and were accepted with minimum cordiality.

Sikhs gave us space to sleep on the gym floor and nothing else. To thwart mosquitoes I tried pitching my pup tent in there and learned that was impossible – needs earth for the pegs. We assured ourselves of pleasant dreams that night by catching *The Rise and Fall of Idi Amin* at the local movie theater.

Here is another good spot to step out of the story and take stock. What happened to the guy recently intimidated by the prospect of Africa, no idea what he's going to do there or how? I'll tell you what happened. He stepped onto the continent and one thing kept leading to another. He acclimated, taking it all in stride now like he owns the joint, stay in a Sikh temple, go to the movies, whatever. After all, it is still planet Earth, not Mars; breathable atmosphere, plenty of water, nice people.

Our third day we awoke on the floor and went to Hippo Point, where I pointed at a Hippo. I have to say, I've been to Hippo Point but I never saw a hippo point. That's what they call a paradox. I did see a three-foot long monitor lizard snatch a daydreaming frog from a rock and then swim toward an island in Lake Victoria, holding the screaming victim by one leg. For whom the frog told, I wondered. A protector who lived eons ago? An eater of monitor lizards? Me?

We returned to the temple and were presented a cookie each with the same mysterious flavor as the tea of Lloyangalani. I took my first temple shower and followed Terry's lead by keeping a diary, which is why this part is so detailed. Despite our inroads we were not invited to dinner so out to eat under a fantastic stormy sky. We watched the sunset then ran through rain to eat sam-osas, kabobs and fries. A delightful surprise, we returned to sleep in our own room on beds. We would have enjoyed all this even more without Uganda hanging over us like a dental appointment.

We awoke once again in Kisumu, said "Adios" to the Sikhs, left a small donation and received that most lavish of compliments, an invitation to return any time. We walked through the industrial part of town, then got a lift with an Indian who took us for a lovely ride to his sugar cane processing plant. Along the way we saw many smiling faces. These people generally looked happier than people anywhere else I've been including Disneyworld. In spirit they resembled far more the happy looking costumes strolling around than the customers. I wondered if it feels simply marvelous and liberating for a black person to come here from the U.S. and suddenly be in the majority, no longer inundated by up-tight Caucasians. I wonder exactly what factors caused the American Indians to be wiped out on their native land while Africans were simply dragged off theirs, but never eradicated from it. Maybe Africa was less desirable as real estate or just too big.

We toured the plant where it's all done by hand, nothing like the monstrous, stinky sugar cane plants in Florida. We had a tea and then headed to Busia: Kenya customs and Goodbye incriminating currency declaration form. Time to start on a new one.

Busia was an unabashed black market for Kenya shillings. We were offered two-hundred fifty Uganda shillings for one Kenya shilling (ten cents American). The bank rate was eighty. We had heard three-hundred could be had in country so I changed only a small amount. Once in Uganda Terry continued changing small because he always hoped to be across the border the next day. This cost him a lot of aggravation, finding transport out taking longer than expected. He was always looking for someone to change more money and it is an illegal activity.

Of course as soon as we shed our Kenya currency declaration forms we were incriminating ourselves in Uganda. But in Uganda it was much more worthwhile. I was under this cloud my entire time in Africa but it seemed to lack lightning. The border guards never really checked.

Into Uganda

A possible explanation ahead of time:

This is a good place to mention that I never have been suicidal nor do I have a death wish as some silly people have suggested. I enjoy being me far too well for that sort of nonsense. (Suppose I came back as a Republican. Then I would really kick myself.) But many of my actions as a grown person could give testimony to the contrary. Uganda was fertile ground for this behavior and I am forced to consider that my third grade teacher was onto something. Like Jed Clampett used to say thoughtfully of Jethro, "There's something wrong with that boy."

That's all it is. Mostly okay, just something a little wrong. It's not that uncommon.

From all accounts Ugandans were terrific even by African standards. Never were they spoken of without allusions to their personal warmth. Even travelers who had ripped the Sudan and crossed only a tiny corner of Uganda en-route to Kenya claimed this brief sojourn as the best of their journey.

This waylaid our fears but little. We never figured it was the Welcome Wagon we had to worry about. I felt as a mullet might, swimming into a school of barracuda.

The police at the border got us a mutatu ride into the stricken land, two innocents in the back seat looking at each other. Off we went with a song in our hearts and our hearts in our mouths but no song in our mouths. I don't know how that can be. Maybe your heart has to stay put for the song to get in your mouth. Anyway that's how it was. With a different anatomy we'd have been singing a song, maybe *The Caissons* or *Over the Rainbow*. Or how about *The Eye of the Tiger.* That would have been good, showed 'em we weren't scairt. But we could barely even mumble.

I was preoccupied with surviving the ride. Expecting the driver to veer off the road at any time and try to kill us or deliver us to people who would, I was considering ways to thwart his dastardly plan. At what point does he show his hand? Should we attack him now? Is Terry going to be any help? Shouldn't one of us be in the front seat? How could we be so stupid, both of us getting in the back like fish in a barrel? Do I go for the cabby or the weapon and why do I have to go to the stupid Serengeti anyway? I imagine the driver would have been more nervous than we were if privy to my thoughts.

Perhaps you're thinking, "Christ on a cupcake! If you're such a big scaredy cat about it, why go? The Serengeti isn't that important. You can see wildlife in Kenya."

As I type this I'm wondering the same thing. Maybe I don't think things through; or it's the potent lure of famous places; or maybe it's just the appeal of a roller coaster - a thrilling ride that deep down you believe you'll survive. I dunno. We all do counter-intuitive stuff.

Even though a cab driver of sorts, he turned out not a murderer. We had still to learn not to fear civilians or the Uganda police who were warm, conscientious public servants unfortunately outgunned by the enemy. Early into the longest three weeks of my life, I would learn to distinguish uniforms. For the first time ever I would welcome the sight of police. After Terry and I parted, it was the cruel, stupid countenance of those in army fatigues I learned to loathe and dread. Oddly no one seemed sure who they were or where they'd come from.

Our first stop en route to the capital was Jinja, a town near one of the supposed sources of the Nile. We rode there without incident, only two roadblocks, manned by the blue uniformed police and all smiles and we relaxed a little. Our motel had the reassuring name The New Safe Restaurant and Lodging. The owner himself was less so. "It's worse now," he lamented. "At least under Amin there had been some control." Sounds like he read the same National Geographic as me.

We thought this an incredible opinion and concluded he must be a bad sort who liked Amin. Terry and I have been in country about an hour and we feel qualified to judge a man whose opinion has been shaped over years by immersion in the subject. It's good to realize how ignorantly people rush to conclusions so we may be skeptical, first and foremost, of our own.

We viewed the source of the Nile from a nearby hillside and it's a view I can no more forget than adequately describe. If a river were a hurricane, it would look like this, swirling around a small island on its way to Egypt, amid lush green hillsides.

The middle of our first night in Uganda featured an attempt to bash into our room from the adjoining one but we guessed they were only drunk and thought it a door. We awoke locked in, lending greater gravity to the attempted visit; unsettling considering our Amin-loving innkeeper. Still I was tempted to stay awhile but next day we rode to Kampala, the source of the Nile tugging at me. I had intended to exit Uganda as quickly as possible but that was starting to change.

Idi Amin ran out all non-Ugandans living in the country. This included Indians, who apparently had formed the backbone of the economy, many born there. None had returned.

Tanzania invaded Uganda in 1979, shelling the capital and routing the dire dictator who took his booty and vacationed in Saudi Arabia. This left a vacuum of evil only too happily filled by something worse. Too bad. It must have seemed a swell idea at the time.

Kampala

I read that Europeans had voted Kampala "Most Beautiful African Capital." In the city of bombed-out buildings we rolled into, a cholera epidemic was ensconced. The only remnant we saw of colonial glory was a street lined with lovely pink-flowered trees.

On the edge of town a roadblock was manned by Tanzanian police, one of whom coveted my oft admired Townsend's Fish House and Tavern t-shirt showing a rotting, flyblown fish emerging from a partly opened sardine can. In a lukewarm stab at pillaging, he insinuated that he should have it. He was not overbearing and accepted with grace my denial.

The previous summer in Europe a gobsmacked German had asked with wonder, "Is that a real place???"

It was real alright. Townsend's – there was a vindication of civilization. A local lawyer of the same name renovated an old two story warehouse and filled it with rubber sharks, anchors, buoys, pilings, boats, fishing tackle, black & white photos from the good old days when you could keep 'em all, always a fun band like Derek and the Slammers and to ice the cake, nurses popping in after their three to eleven shift. You want respite from first floor festivities? Walk upstairs to the cozy, quiet bar in the large library – every single book a hardcover classic. You want to read a little? Just blindly grab one, find a comfy chair. It never mattered if you spent any money. You could go to Townsend's only to read in public. It was in their parking lot that I emerged victorious and unscathed from my one and only pissing contest. Sometimes I made the wardrobe error of donning my white briefs after my jeans and going Superman style which upped the fun amazingly. There was even this guy in a suit who'd drop slacks to ankles and shuffle around the place in boxers as an expression of his love for all humanity.

Wishing to lose consciousness before 2 a.m. in the new millennium, after twenty years Clay sold it. He was immediately sorry from the other side of the fence where he was able to see the place transcended his need for sleep. The new owner shut it down, no lingering decay and death by neglect, maybe the way it had to be.

We stayed on The Tourist Hotel, one of the few lodgings in Kampala with running water, recommended by an American woman I met in Nairobi. The hotel water was potable although the air turned out a bit dangerous.

Causes for cholera were apparent. From my rooftop I could see kids playing behind the hotel in stagnant water. I left my passport at the Rwanda embassy for a visa and had to stay in Kampala until it was ready.

No rooms were available, occupied by eight Africans from neighboring countries who seemed to be businessmen; and two American reporters: Mark Lee working for the London Daily Telegraph and Tom? a reporter for BBC, Reuters. Mark was a little guy and Tom stocky. Mark had been there several months and he seemed about to crack up. Of course I never knew him before. Hill, the British writer kidnapped and held hostage by Amin and who played himself in the movie we'd seen still got his mail at The Tourist Hotel and we just missed him.

Mark Lee filled me in on buying batiks, quilts, coffee and changing money. I suspected this was less to help me shop than to get business for his Ugandan friends. I could have spared myself trouble by changing more at the border. I rarely got a better rate. Three hundred could be had for large sums but money stretched so far it was impossible to spend an appreciable amount.

I ate at the Eagle Cafe and pined for Jinja. Trying to call home from the hotel was an exercise in futility. We bedded down for our first night atop Kampala and right away its charms were revealed. Few accommodations offer this caliber of ambiance. The reporters suggested dodge-bullet, a game of chance played while walking to the bedroll to turn in, utilizing stray machine gun fire. I wasn't sure they weren't pulling my leg, but felt it best to assume they weren't. All nocturnal movements were performed stooped. As a bonus, if unable to sleep, we could count sheep blown to bits bounding over the fence. We judged by the loudness of the bursts if they were encroaching, always rooting for the fading of the rat-a-tat-tat, something I didn't appreciate before. Here is another great boon of traveling - accumulating new things to appreciate. This put me in a small subset of Americans my age who avoided Viet Nam but still can appreciate lack of machine gun fire.

New York has pigeons. Ominously and appropriately marabou storks, a long legged carrion bird, stalked rooftops across this city. They could see me on the rooftop I stalked.

Mark was an addict and he told me it is easy to become addicted because it's everywhere. He added that it's a very common addiction among foreigners who stay awhile. He was addicted to the Uganda people. Eventually I understood that.

He arranged for a batiker, Francis Wasswa, to meet me on the roof. I bought several fantastic pieces which I sent home by surface mail, cheap anyway but with the black market exchange rate it was virtually free. Amid the chaos the post office functioned with impunity. It makes you wonder if post offices are some international conspiracy that operates autonomously, set up long ago by world travelers who required communication.

A secure place to leave the pack is a priceless boon to a foot traveler especially when it's a burden like mine. As it happened a family of Ugandans was living in a lean-to on the roof. I could leave my pack with them and they would guard it and shelter it from rain. Here were people of little means who viewed me as someone they could help. This allowed me to stroll freely to the market where wonderfully delicious pineapples were sold.

Concurring with the nefarious Jinja hotel owner who preferred Amin to the current president, Mark said he could show me places around Kampala where hundreds of Milton Obote's supposed enemies had been dumped.

The streets and sidewalks eerily emptied by five o'clock; the capital of a country and not a soul abroad until the next day. From my perch I was like a sentry over a ghost town. Once shortly after five I saw a person dart between buildings; for evening beckoned forth the marauders who roamed like fun-loving zombies, shooting anything that moved and, wanting that, shooting buildings.

{I freely note here that this absolutely is not my mug of Ovaltine. I found that I don't like Cretins, as Mark referred to them, willy-nilly shooting guns off around me; especially since I was, as Irmin Opper had quaintly put it, "without defense." A lot underwhelmed, I wanted to talk to the folks back home. There was one telephone in the hotel and you put your name and the phone number in a queue. Someone would try to place the call and if successful you would be called to the phone. This dragged on for hours. There I would be with a backdrop of machine gun bursts, not so certain as usual of my prospects and wholeheartedly wishing to hear the voice of a sibling. Just to make that flimsy connection would have been comforting. The failed attempts were frustrating and the time I got through to my sister was heartbreaking. Four a.m. Florida time, hubby answered the phone and hung up. I learned later that he said it was "just some Cuban or something." Eventually I got through to my brother in Memphis who thought it was a joke and almost hung up.}

Without a tent, Terry was affronted because I wouldn't let him use mine as a canopy to repel the dew as we slept. He was aggravated more when I was right and there was no dew. Oddly this opened a rift between us. Having gotten each other to

Kampala alive, we ceased operating as a pair, each getting up to different things.

Following is a real authentical transcription of my short-lived journal. We had arrived on Saturday:

Sunday -

Awoke on roof without “demon dew” as I expected, placed call to M.A. - answered phone but instead of M.A. was someone calling to tell Mark that troops had been deployed throughout city – Mark (working for Daily Telegraph) scopes situation – explains soldiers surround P.O. and telecommunications but not radio so no big deal. Meanwhile I have awakened M.A. At 4 a.m. Dull Sunday, marabou storks sinisterly walking the rooftops, another reporter from BBC, Reuters etc. comes zooming into the parking lot on his motorcycle, waves goodbye to a group in a white (police escort) car and arrives upstairs where he breathlessly describes a recent occurrence which will be related herein, henceforth – riding blissfully around the roundabout he's faced with an automatic weapon protruding from a car with five fellows in it. - they want his bag and his bike – he gives the bag but turns the bike off and they can't start it. As the fellow with the gun looks quizzically at the bike the reporter trots off – About the time he hits the bushes an army warrant officer who has spied the situation takes a shot with his pistol which then jams – at this point the reporter is going like hell, scares some farmer out of his field, as the sound of shots fades into the background, the shots being a round let off by the surprised bandit into the ground – the police retreat but the army guy returns in 15 minutes with 2 truckloads of soldiers - “We'll get 'em!” Sometime or another in all this a woman was shot – reporter chastises self for not carrying a gun and being a hero – a dead hero, I add – good for the storks. 2nd attempt in 2 days on his bike - 1st was merely sneak-thief – author's note all occurred within 300 –

500 meters of major police station – got closer with each telling – journalistic license, I presume. Today I continue to lay low.

Next day – new pen – Monday

Numerous futile attempts to change money – ride through town facing backwards on Tom's motorcycle to meet fascinating woman of the quilts – news of looting and raping and pillaging 30 km from here – tomorrow Mark goes there. See presidential escorts – truck with bazooka, soldiers with gas masks on, one demonstrates his playfulness and waggles a rocket launcher in my face, others waving handguns at general population – many carrion birds circling today. Marabou storks everywhere. Called Arnie this morning. Much (by my standards) shooting last night. Have learned that I prefer shooting stars at night. What a crazy place – police and soldiers paid nothing – 800 – 1000 sh. What costs me a dollar (a meal) costs them over three dollars.

Tomorrow – change some money – 20$ - see quilt woman – buy and send coffee – Repay Tom and Terry

I interrupt these journal excerpts with the news that I found a place where lorries congregate and got Terry a ride. So long Terry. Already my diary-uh is fading – no entries for two days. It's funny how even in a place like this, pretty soon there's nothing new to write about. Tom's motorcycle was the last available one in Kampala, an available vehicle being one that hasn't been stolen yet.

Next noteworthy day – Thurs. -

Greeted in the morn by a very nice sunrise and soldiers. Naturally I was delighted finally to hear the fateful words, “You are wanted at the police station.” “Why?” I asked - “All people such as you are wanted there.” Saved, believe it or not, by that beautiful little piece of paper obtained at the Uganda high commission in Nairobi. Still a free man, unlike eight...

What's the point of including a diary without interrupting it? The reader must be wondering what "people such as you" meant. It meant people without passport, no matter mine was at the Rwanda embassy doing what passports do. What I wished most to avoid had got me. I was being arrested. Oddly enough I had prepared myself for this eventuality.

Nairobi had been rife with rumors about what papers were required for travel into and around Uganda and Tanzania including official police permission to return from Tanzania to Kenya; so I had obtained every paper and passport stamp. This included an impressive looking document with the Uganda High Commission as the letterhead. I happened to think of it and whipped it out. Though it meant little, when I held it up, it was as a picture of Rosie O'Donnell to a vampire. In Africa, I learned, image can be everything. I would continue my trip unrobbed.

A short concrete wall surrounded my roof with small openings that made a design, perfect for my135 mm lens. Later that morning through one of the holes I photographed people being removed from a building across the street by soldiers and loaded into a Uganda Bookmobile van, of all things, to be robbed at the police station. Had I been discovered, my immunity may have expired along with my camera. Already I had met on the street an American who claimed he had just emerged from two weeks solitary confinement without food. He said he had been once in the army so authorities suspected him of being a mercenary.

Kampala market

Rooftop Views

The old roundup

Kampala at 5 o'clock

Francis Wasswa

Home sweet home

Kabalega Falls National Park

Back to the diary -

...others at the hotel. I take care of business and head the hell out of Kampala, in the process of which I receive almost inconceivable kindness from the police – from my first inquiry as to which way to go I'm passed from hand to hand and never on my own again, right down to a personal escort back to Kampala after brave attempts at getting me a ride, and to the Speke Hotel as they felt I would not be safe from the soldiers on my former perch. At this moment I have been placed in the hands of a man who is resident here and will try to negotiate me a spot in the lounge, free of charge. Here I am, after my interview and my meal, recalling the day. I asked one policeman how his rifle worked so he took the cartridge off, took aim and shot a passing motorist – much laughter – Later – his words, pleading my case as I stand in the rain - “Assist him! He's a man like you!” fell on deaf ears – other policeman, in truck, is “not a kind man.” Other – Michael Emor – policeman asks me to take his picture – poses very sternly. Other – Michael's brother – buys me a Pepsi which I end up paying for. Mailed everything off today – Took surreptitious photos this morning. Both Toms had no passport this morning. Recalling yesterday's ride backward through Kampala. Soldiers search places so they can loot. Speke Hotel, my present lodging, will accept only foreign currency. Just received a proposition, I think – she doesn't believe I'm sleeping on the floor – Izrael – room

Further diary interruption -

Rwanda visa secured, I have decided to be a man about it and check out Uganda a little bit, though it's a stingy visa granting me only a few weeks to get there. The reporters recommended Kabalega Falls National Park as the safest place to go so that's where I'm heading. The best thing about Kampala was the pineapples.

Michael's brother had insisted I stay in a roadside shelter while he stood in the rain in his slicker trying to get me a ride. He also insisted that I sit rather than stand. At four o'clock I still was there and Michael returned. They judged it unwise for me to be on the road so late in the day so Michael brought me back to the city. He made me wait for him outside the police station while he checked out and then he brought me to the Speke Hotel.

Friday -

Back out the old roadblock – today Tanzanian police – one wants a shirt – they're trying to get me a ride – then my friend from yesterday comes along – Michael's brother – Soon I'm on the bus – my first taste of waragy – goes down very easily, also good music – stop at great little market – pineapple sections, broiled meat, banana cookies – extremely cheap – shish-k-bob – ten sh. - Onward to park entrance – cross bridge get first view of Victoria Nile – great – wait around entrance, learn of ranger's problems at home, caught two poachers recently, eat simsim seeds – fried, pounded then crushed – great -like p-nut butter – have "Bell" Uganda beer with army officer – oddly he gets ranger to fetch beer for him – fantastic beer even warm – declare it best I've ever had – learn his philosophy – won't stand for looting – problem is soldiers left without officers – shortage of officers - good to learn of his views – take photos of everyone – into park in back of Land Rover – good ride – meet Billy, finish beer – meet warden – set up camp - much shooting in the night at the gate.

Third diary interruption -

The bus ride north was an experience unto itself, quite a party. Lots of friendly Ugandans, I had my first local moonshine, made from sugar cane. It actually got too cold for my clothes and I wound up sitting in the aisle near the engine, a little warmer.

Finally crossing the bridge near the park entrance in the back of a truck, I caught a glimpse of the White Nile. A raging tumult of multi-colored chaos, it had picked up a lot of turbidity since Jinja. At the gate to Chobe sector an army officer got a ranger to fetch me a brew while we sat in his hut and chatted, clearly demonstrating the pecking order.

An unusual looking man with olive skin and egg size vertical eyes drooping from the face of a giant kudu I would one day walk up on, he told me the problem with the country was soldiers without officers; said he himself wouldn't stand for looting. His demeanor was reassuring but later in my trip I would see officers themselves striking fear into a town.

Come dark some rangers drove out to shuttle me into the park. Riding in the back of the Land Rover, watching our dust and finishing a beer, I was feeling just so darn good, don't know exactly why. Maybe because I found myself welcomed and no longer on my own. The only incident was a holdup by a band of lions refusing to relinquish the road. They were just lion there. For the first time I was in a place where lion is a pun instead of a metaphor.

I was ejected near the rangers' quarters and pitched my tent under the only tree, a fine spot in most places, not so fine there. I would learn of things to keep off one's tent worse than sun and dew. The annoying ranger Billy took me under his wing, a place I had no wish to be. I can only conjecture that he was familiar with or had heard of big spenders who visited the park in its heyday. It was apparent immediately that he would prevent me meeting Warden Akena so as not to lose his grip. His plan was ill-disguised and I made sure he delivered me.

There was much shooting that night at the gate, random shooting like an aspect of the weather report now: Partly violent with a twenty percent chance of early shooting rising to eighty percent after dark, will feel like ninety, etc. In the morning I was brought to Warden Akena's house. Apprised that he was on Amin's hit list, the warden had exiled himself in Sudan for some years and had only just returned. He'd sent a ranger to investigate the shooting and was on the radio talking about it when I walked in but we never did find out what had occurred.

Yes, that's right. I said "we." There's no excluding anybody. When you get out there in Uganda, I found, there are no observers. You're in it up to your eyeballs – or higher. No info withheld, everybody's a stakeholder.

Then Akena got down to brass tacks and let me know what he really wanted from me. He'd taken photos in years prior with no way to get them processed, wondered if I might work that charm. I know well the keen desire to see the photos so I hated to disappoint him with my limited abilities. Probably too long in the can anyway.

The tourist industry having folded years before with the onset of Idi Amin, the park was almost completely overgrown. Soldiers had long since machine-gunned all the pet lions. Without tourists the only job for rangers was poacher control. Their policy was to capture poachers armed with crude weapons and to ambush and kill poachers with guns. There are two parts to Kabalega Falls National Park: Chobe Sector and Paraa Sector. I was in Chobe.

The rangers are a rare breed of Africans who love animals and that is why they are rangers. It sure ain't the pay. One of them was faced with giving up his career because his brother had died so he must go and care for his brother's family.

I met the big friendly Ugandan who ran the rangers' store. His three wives were spread out at intervals across the countryside; distance being, according to him, essential to harmony. We agreed that if I could provide fish, his on-site wife would prepare it for us.

I felt confident of my end though I had yet to wet a line in the Nile.

Absurdly the lodge by the river was open and functioning, lacking only customers, catering to the occasional dignitary. One night some U.N. guy from Holland invited me up to his room for drinks. He poured me a few Scotches as I impressed myself in a conversation on world affairs. Sometimes it's not what you don't know but where you don't know it. Meeting in Orlando, he correctly dismisses me as just another ignorant bumpkin. But in this setting, with a dearth of Caucasians about, he plies me with Scotch for my opinion and offers me his.

Once more I tout the benefits of going. And going along for the ride. This stuff doesn't happen when you're sitting in your house watching a documentary. I find amazing my involvement in a world beyond my imagining and obviously beyond my ability to plan. I'm this guy who lives in Orlando suddenly hanging out with African soldiers, United Nations representatives, Uganda park rangers and more. These people and this place were like a fairy tale never read and just by going, it all has come alive around me, vastly deepening and eventually darkening the scope of my life and knowledge of my home planet. And from their viewpoint, I have materialized illogically in their midst, proof of a place as hidden from them as this was from me; a modern, secure place that I have eschewed for theirs, the one country where I was sure I would not set foot.

Tossing Beetle Spin and squirrel tail jig into eddies behind the building, I was delighted to quickly catch three Nile perch, a couple pounds each. Only on presenting my catch did I realize how skeptical the astounded store keeper had been of my ability to produce. Modern tackle is quite an advantage.

Those three fish were a cheap ticket to a fascinating dining experience and a lesson in domestic order. Our meal was served by his lame wife who did all the traveling while we sat on the ground in the hut. First she brought soap and a basin for us to wash our hands. Next the fish arrived, served in a vat of juices with casava on the side. Casava is a sort of yam as appealing a la carte' as styrofoam. And as moist. You collect some casava, punch a bowl in it with your thumb and scoop juices with it.

Again I caught the perch, this time with my hands. They were dead and in a vat so it was easy, though sticky. My host felt that metal utensils would spoil the flavor. A rationalization for not having them? I doubt it. Disliking the stickiness at first, I got used to it. It was a satisfying meal and healthful. When we were done the pleasant lady and model of correct womanhood limped to us once more with soap and a new basin of water.

My idle hours were butt to ground under my tree, with ranger Billy, apparently without duties, making a Herculean attempt at getting a chair under me. Sure his canary was suffering without a perch, he constantly hovered about with this little chair, ready to pounce at the first clear opportunity. Or he'd slyly place it near me like a tropical fish enthusiast sets a castle and anxiously watches for his pet to occupy it. Telling him I wished no chair had no more effect than trying to blow away the wind. The silly man hoped that after enough pestering, I'd sit on the thing to satisfy him and indebt myself. I wouldn't have minded a chair but darned if it would be his.

I knew Billy did not really wish me well and would be happiest seeing me perched on fresh rhino dung. Or under it. He considered himself a fisherman, his tackle a handline and baited hook, and he had presaged my baitless defeat by the Nile. He received with ill-disguised (again) contempt news of his river's treachery.

Hoping to keep everything from eating his tourist, the warden prohibited me strolling alone so next morning a ranger took me on a riverside trek. It was pretty hot but even where we saw no crocs I wasn't allowed a dip in the inviting torrent. Crocodiles savvy predators, there were only specific spots where the rangers bathed, none of them along our route.

The White Nile there is a striking blue-green bordered by

verdant hillsides and thick jungle often topped by pendulous gray clouds. As we strolled the bank without fishing tackle, one exciting virgin eddy after another enticing me, an unwise plan was forming for the next day.

Returning, we strayed from the river into view of a herd of black buffalo, Africa's most dangerous animal. Every year they teach lots of Africans a lesson they'll never remember. They also dispatch the occasional great white hunter who irritates one by shooting it, from much the same impulse that we swat a mosquito.

As it happens the Uganda crowd are the most deadly with a fifty percent kill rate per attack. I have since read accounts of these bullies pounding the Cheerios out of people from sheer animosity for our species, even knocking them out of trees to do it. Appraising these things on teevee doesn't render justice. They're huge, hulking slabs. A tall snob's nose would not reach the nape of the neck. My protector waved his AK-47 and his arms over his head and when they only looked our way and chuckled, he got this real scared look and said, "We'd better get out of here."

Then I knew the benefit of him and his pea shooter: if we're lucky enough to be charged by only one behemoth, half a chance it goes for the other fleeing figure. This dilemma calls up the worst in a person, for who among us would not wish his guide, County Commissioner, perhaps even spouse to be the chosen one? Isn't it better to give than receive sympathy? In the lead would you throttle back to even the odds or embrace your role in natural selection and pour on the coals?

In Florida the wildlife is pretty kumbaya. Even alligators are timid and I don't mind sharing the water with them, having spent many idyllic days walking, running and wading barefoot the upper St. Johns River, occasionally meeting cattle and the rare assertive steer. So I was used to going wherever I liked in quest of fish, not yet fully appreciating my change in circumstances.

Next morning, like I had done as a boy, I rose ahead of the sun to escape sleeping authority and go fishing. It always had a downside in Orlando; but here, if I'd had the time, I would have regretted it with all my heart.

After success behind the lodge, I expected to pull a Nile perch from every excellent looking hole. Inexplicably this did not happen. In fact all day was required to come up with a couple for dinner.

A black buffalo wallowing on the shore halted me for awhile. Only after seeing an egret soar in and disrespectfully light on its head did I judge the beast decrepit and feel safe skirting it. Farther along I became hot and took the longed-for dip in the beautiful water, though it was spoiled by the prospect of a crocodile enjoying it more. Along the way were many hippos and a big water snake.

Returning by the river, I saw giraffe heads far off in the bush and started off cross country toward them, perhaps to see if they were attached to anything.

{At this point the reader may be about to slam shut the book, thinking, "Buffalopoop! It's bad enough you're just like Pollyanna, all la-dee-dah strolling along the Nile fishing, your only concern in the world being that they're not biting. As a sumptuous hunk of live bait being trolled along the shore, you should be *very glad they're not biting!* 'But now let's go check out the giraffes.' Nobody is this stupid."

I'm getting a little tired of constantly having to remind the faithless reader that this is a truthful narrative and "stupid" may be a bit harsh. It's far easier to imagine someone being significantly ignorant of the potential for things to go wrong. There. That's better now isn't it? And if that weren't the case this story would have far less interesting predicaments to explore.}

Yes, it did seem to be the area where the black buffaloes had been but it's not every day I get to see giraffes walking around so, exercising the popular human prerogative of substituting optimism for judgment, I figured probably the buffaloes wouldn't be there two days in a row. I mean what are the odds? In my life I've seen a herd of black buffaloes one time. Now I'm going to start seeing them every day? In the same spot?

Ridiculous. Anyway, yesterday we'd seen them from afar, way before we would have gotten to them. I hadn't seen a sign of them this time. No tracks, no BUFFALOES arrow, no black buffalo flag painting the breeze. Looks like an all clear to me.

Of course if this were nowadays and I was putting out some kind of a live feed, here is the point where people would start yelling, "Don't do that." Hopefully.

This episode also illustrates how poorly served we are by our constricted viewpoint compared to, say, an eagle, who can be surprised by nothing on the ground. We get a comparable view of the sky, preparing us for the weather and the arrival of space aliens. Denied the aerial view showing what lies ahead in time to alter course, always we must get there to find out. Perhaps the lucky people of the future will venture forth with a drone.

As far as I know, I was right. On arriving I saw no herd. I continued toward the giraffes, having a nice optimistic time and it's like the buffalo exploded out of the ground. I'm gonna call him Bill. Bill erupted in front of me in a cloud of dust and a hearty hi-yo Silver and stopped in his tracks glaring down at the interloper. Apparently the herd left and didn't tell him where they were going. This, incidentally, is the worst case scenario. A lone black buffalo, I had read, normally is a male outcast, of naturally ill temper even for his species, exacerbated by his current shunning. And he'd love just to take it all out on something soft and annoying like a human.

To my credit I knew immediately that this could really hurt. In fact I savvied that I probably had killed myself and that hurt more than anything. If I would manage to outlive Mozart was out of my hands. Right here, right now, by any metric excluding some bad-ass guardian angels, this is the fate set by my first step toward the Freddie Laker airplane. I had no business being in Uganda and this proved it. Continued life would be at the pleasure of this Billious buffalo and anything I went on to, fun, fishing, romance, more fishing, would flow from his call. Should he justify his reputation by murdering me, there would be no investigation, no trial and no comeuppance. There ain't no law agin it. Other species get away with murder – murder of each other, murder of us. Killing within the species – that's what raises the human eyebrow. Buffalo on human, that's nature. Human on human – what's up with that? Fair enough, we get to murder them too, because courtroom justice is impractical.

The line-up would be tricky. "Do any of these buffaloes look familiar?"

"All of 'em."

"So. It was a conspiracy. Arrest the lot."

And then the trial:

"Why did you do it?"

(silence) x 5

"Where were you on the afternoon of August 30th?"

(silence)

"Don't try to buffalo me."

The frustrated public defender: "What do you expect? They're buffaloes!"

"Objection!"

"Sustained. Council will refrain from using exclamation points."

"What?? *He* just used one."

The prosecutor: "Objection."

"Sustained. Council will refrain from double question marks."

"What?? They can't talk. You're railroading them!"

The judge: "Alright, that's it. Guilty. Execute the black one."

The prosecutor: "They're all black. They're black buffaloes."

"Then execute the lot. We'll let God snort them out."

The Public defender: "I object to such punishment."

The judge: "Too little, too late."

And then there'd be the litany of appeals. It just wouldn't be deemed worth it. Perhaps after the universal translator is invented.

The best I could realistically hope for was a retro Darwin Award. (I did not actually consider all these things right then but saved them for a more appropriate time, years later.)

However I still had an opportunity to influence this buffalo's decision. Though my body was panicking not in the way you're thinking, my brain was on the problem, to quote the indomitable sage Festus Hagen, like ugly on ape. I take it this was my survival instinct showing up at the last second, as usual.

"Hey - better late than never," my instinct says.

"Nice old adage," I retort. "But how about this – a stitch in time saves nine?"

"Yeah, that's a good one, very appropriate. I was resting. Can't be on all the time like the Battery Bunny. How about using those 'higher cognitive functions' a little more?"

"We'll discuss it later. How about getting us out of this fix right now? That's your specialty."

The next thing I knew, three options flashed through my head simultaneously:

A. If you want to threaten a monster, if that's what you really want to do, continue walking into its space like you're bad or something because as we know, it's all shits and giggles until somebody giggles and shits. (I wasn't feeling that irascible on this day, having walked quite far; and really, if I walked any farther, I'd bump into him).

B. If you'd like a monster to chase you, run from it (once again a bit tired).

C. If you'd like to die a thousand deaths culminating in the one final and completely fatal heart attack, leaving the folks back home forlorn, take the middle ground and stop and stand there (this would have ruined my trip).

All this was processed instantly and I knew that only one move remained. Fortunately I'd seen it work for... “and now, with no further adieu we give you that renowned adventurer, the King of Cool, let's hear it for ... Bugs Bunny!” from whom I take most of my direction in life. That's right. You knew you'd seen it somewhere. Mid-step I pivoted around in one smooth motion and continued that step at the original pace but the opposite way as unruffled as a plucked chicken, as though I'd simply gone as far as I cared to and was about to retrace my steps anyway. Only by conjuring a yawn and suddenly learning to whistle could I have displayed less concern.

If you can imagine the combined urgency of a team of horses tethered to a heavy object, say, the Lincoln Memorial, with the Wizard of Oz shoving red hot coals up their rumps, then you have a good imagination; and some idea of the caliber of effort my legs were willing to put into a sprint. I believe this was the best opportunity I ever would have to find out if I could take off and fly.

It's good the body is ruled by one authority or each part of mine would have been performing a different trick and probably I would have exploded there on the spot. Then Bill really would have had something to brag about if they ever let him back in the herd - “Yeah, I was just standing there looking at it and the damn thing blew up.”

“They sure don't make 'em like they used to,” an elder wryly observes.

“Don't give me that hippo doo-doo, you old buffalo fart. This was the same thing. Just like that one you stamped out back when you weren't so old.”

“But I did have to stomp it before it came apart.”

“That's right! *You* had to touch it. I got the stare. That's the new way. You don't touch 'em. You stare 'em apart.” And then he shows everybody the stare.

A teenager says, “I don't think it's the stare. I think you killed it with your breath."

Then they all had a good horse-laugh.

He might have gotten endless mileage out of that anecdote, maybe they make him leader of the herd, like Rudolph with his red shnoz. Then a song gets written about him and he's beloved by children everywhere. Don't seem right somehow.

To the tune of Rudolph -

Billy the big mean buffalo
didn't need no shiny nose
all he had to do was stand there
and he could make a man explode.

Yeah, yeah, yeah...you can compose the remaining verses. The whole thing's starting to tick me off.

Back to the tourist -

Never has a less helpful landscape cruelly presented itself to one pining to scamper up a tree, a bean stalk, the side of a building or a social ladder. To a lifelong fan of down, up never looked so good. Thorn trees abounded but not even a charging black buffalo will send me into one of those.

Surely the reader has known moments when there was one particular sound he most did not want to hear, like the crash of that tree in front of you into your car. All the other sounds in the world, no problem. Not asking a lot. Just that one thing you truly could do without right now; so you can relate to my feelings as I strolled away from that heaving mass of lethalness, longing for a decent tree to climb, wishing to be most anywhere else on the planet and I heard it start to run. That was the thing, in case you're wondering, that I didn't want to hear. I had yearned only for hooves to remain silent. Of the vast array of sounds I was prepared to tolerate, even welcome - a German dixieland band for God's sake. Bring it on. Roseanne Barr farting, Joel Osteen, you name it really, instead I heard the giant beast charging me and I had no place to go and no point trying to outrun it through that vast expanse of nothing to climb that faced me. Too often the dearth wins over the plethora and two legs just can't compete with four.

I stuck with the plan suggested by my tardy survival instinct, not looking back, casually placing one foot before the other, anticipating at every moment the horn ride. When that begins I'll wish I had at least tried to outrun it, or ride it.

As eternity approaches, some people see a blazing white light or a golden door. Or their life flashes before them. Should you choose not to believe what I am about to reveal, I won't blame you. I can hardly believe it myself. With Buffalo Bill bringing up the rear, in front of me appeared Porky The Pig stuttering, "That's all f..." He never got it all out. Lucky thing he stutters. (Once you open the door to Looney Tunes, apparently there's no closing it. But I will try. I don't see any way Yosemite Sam can get into this story.)

From the vacuum of speech left by The Pig, an ethereal balm of peace and gladness began spreading across my ragged existence, not because I had accepted my premature end but because the folks back home and the future were returning at the same pace as the clippity-clop of the overgrown cheeseburger's hooves was receding. Yes, the big coward actually was charging away. The moment I twigged that the volume knob was turning to the left was one lovely moment, continuing to this day among my all time favorites.

In our brief standoff while I was nonchalantly turning around, he must have noticed what a tough hombre I probably might be. Compared to a very dangerous little girl or a raccoon. Or a clown. Yeah, a real tough clown in a tu-tu. Singing *Tiptoe Through the Tulips*. Tougher than that. I should have played around with him a little more, you know what I mean? Slapped him around. Peed on his leg. Had a little fun with Captain Huff & Puff.

Anyway, you won't get this brand of relief from Pepto Bismol. Upon reaching a real big, climbable tree later on, it felt grand to stand by it, which I did for some time purely for the sensation, silently daring him to try and get me now. All kudus to the survival instinct. And guardian angels. I let the giraffes go for the day.

See how my list of consolation grows. Now, whenever things are going badly and there are also machine guns, I should be able to look around and think, alright. No buffaloes. I could have done that before but it wouldn't have meant much. By day's end I would have another, to cover me in a time of machine guns and buffaloes. Whoopee!

To demonstrate the effort involved in generating an account of events that may be of interest to the reader, I present my diary version:

SUN: rise early. Go where guide took me Sat. - Catch only two fish – see many hippos, old cape buffalo, big water snake, take dip in the dreaded Nile (quick one) – on way back see giraffe, get chased by buffalo – make it back in time for beer -

Looking at it, there's a lot to be said for brevity. Concerning the calling forth of Mr. Osteen, yes, I'm guessing he was barely a twinkle in somebody's eye back then, but I'm writing it now and might be forgiven for broaching the space-time continuum to so powerfully illustrate a point.

A direct result of the foregoing episode, I developed Levine's Law: “Never risk your life when you can have as much fun without risking it.” Unfortunately for me the key to abiding by it is identifying the risk.

A memorable aspect of Uganda sojourning was the pattern of trepidation – relief, trepidation – relief. Trepidation never was long on the heels of relief and so it was this day as the stage was being set for the most fearful night of my life.

Diary continues -

– same thing I had at warden's house – strange stuff – now awaiting meal – informed that my tent scared away an elephant in my absence – eat fish with maize bread – amaizing – Return to the river and fish behind lodge.

{Unfortunately I became inspired to verse and must include it for the integrity of the record.}

Of course my tombstone could extol
All my valorous deeds
But then 'twould be too big.
So I'll rest happy if it simply reads:
Here lies Tom Levine
He caught a Nile perch
on a squirrel tail jig.

Also caught my first Nile catfish – on beetle spin – looked like a jolly blue cat. Later, fishing from rock outcropping. I look back through the trees to see the main bank full of elephants – beautiful sight. I walk over to the main bank and take a couple pictures. After a bit the leader, I suppose, comes over and very politely asks me to go away. I comply.

Diary interruption:

It's true I don't speak elephant but some things are universal. The elephant asked me in this way: He approached me haltingly, taking one and a half steps toward me, then retreating the same distance. During the retreat he would lift his head at me. He did this a few times and I got the message though I barely had time to scramble out before they inundated the area. Back to diary -

Beautiful sunset, elephants trumpeting from the river. I reflect on the good life of a hippo and easily conclude I'd rather be a hippo than a croc. Eat great supper in lodge – beef, potatoes, rice, for less than $1, preceded by 2nd Uganda beer – lacks the impact of my first but still good – people singing Uganda victory songs. I talk to Uganda social scientist who blames soldiers' actions on seeing example of what Amin soldiers could get away with – proclaims me a rare species. Asks me if I'm not afraid of the animals. I reply "Nothing to be afraid of".

Unavoidable diary interruption:

Did you just read that ??!??!?*? Does this idio... er, writer have a short memory or what??? Thing is in this place you don't need a memory with all the reminders you get.

Back to the diary -

Head back to my tent in the dark considering it to have been a full day. (mini- diary interruption - next day Warden Akena would inform me that two days prior a ranger was chased by a lion in exactly the same spot). Awakened in the night. I look out my window and see the lovely silhouette of an elephant reaching up to the branches with its trunk. Ceases to be interpreted by me as a lovely phenomenon as several elephants crowd around my tent. Suddenly I'm waiting for a limb to come crashing down on me.

At this point the camper is suspending direct transcription of the diary that he may use all his resources to help the reader relate to him and his latest plight.

My fortress against the wild animals of the East African night was a beige Eureka Nu-lite backpacking tent. This is a nylon, breathable yet waterproof film without fly purchased by me for the virtues of American stitching, easy set-up, light weight and fifty bucks. There's room inside for two compatible campers to sleep side by side if they don't move and don't fart and ceiling for a short person to sit up in the middle toward either end. A string from the top of an aluminum tube anchors it at each end and aluminum pegs secure the perimeter. It was designed for and very good at repelling tiny things like mosquitoes, ridicule and rain drops. This seemed quite satisfactory until I awoke to the inspiring image.

I found the view flawed, blocked by the massive foot of another colossus planted next to my little back window like a Roman column with pores, my head below knee level. This is all I ever saw of them, prohibited by proximity from viewing the whole leg, like a person trying to see the whole planet by looking straight down. It occurs to me now that seeing the entire problem probably would have been scarier yet. From this I became an "elephant snob." No one can speak to me about the immensity of an elephant without he has been trapped squatting in a small tent in a herd of them. Viewpoint can be everything.

Great. Right? Thought I'd survived this day, dodged that bullet. But nooooo. Rather than just lollygag around, elephants decided to do something with their time and walk over and rip apart the tree sheltering my eggshell. They couldn't have scratched that itch last week or some other night in the last few years, or next week. No, it had to be now, so somebody could testify to their industry. I suppose earlier in the evening it went something like this:

"Whaddaya feel like doin' tonight, Jumbo?"

"I dunno, Dumbo, whadda *you* feel like doin'?"

"I know what *I* feel like doin'."

"Look, Dumbo, I'm thirty-four years old and I've been lookin' for an elly every night since my tusks came in. Mama's always at me -'Get married, when you gonna get married, Jumby? Your little brother just got married.' I'm tired of it. Whatever ellies want, I ain't got."

"I know what you mean. Some of these hippies are startin' to look pretty good."

"It's hippos. They're hippos."

Jumbo looks at his pal sideways. "Ah, we probably couldn't even get one of them."

"You know, you're right. Let's just get the gang together and bust up that tree over by the humans."

"Yeah, sure. Why not?"

And so misdirected testosterone extends its global reign of terror.

I consoled myself with figuring this probably was the herd from the river, a reasonable bunch if ever there was one and not the sort to engage in vandalism of personal property. But even then, one dance move, one misplaced step, one elephant who just doesn't give a rat's ass ... It became an entire night poised on the brink of destruction, anchored in a gale of shitting, farting, pissing, ripping, tearing and trumpeting pachyderms. I'm sure this hardly ever happens to anybody but at the age of thirty-one it was happening to me and I couldn't help feeling it was the culmination of some errant process that began long ago. It was inevitable that one day I would find myself in this fix. I judged that if I were to emerge from the tent to initiate getting the Hello Kitty out of there, it would have been like tossing a big ugly rat into a crowd of women standing around eating ravioli, maybe even worse; so I stayed inside.

That clang you just heard was my bar for success dropping another rung from not having a job to not being dead. It's a fine standard and one I have stuck with, granting me a streak of successful days. On the down side it's very unforgiving. To further reduce my odds for a successful night, the occasional huge limb thudded to the ground. On the Uganda stock exchange TL futures also was plummeting.

{I would like to acknowledge the main drawback with reading this part of the book - the lack of genuine suspense. Most of the suspense hinging on whether or not the main character buys the farm, you're sure every time because dead men tell no tales. It's boring but there's nothing I can do about that now. If it helps you any, I'd enjoy the writing more with the outcome in doubt; but this is *non*-fiction and I'm not going to knock myself off here and there to keep you wondering. Then it would be *fiction*. But - there are other people and you never know when one of them might tip over, so just try to enjoy the story for what it is.}

I sat there shocked and bewildered at this drop in the neighborhood that never in a million years or more would I have predicted and so had not developed a plan to deal with. And really, who would? One always suspects himself smarter than this. I had contemplated other useful contingencies like would I rather be a bass or a tree? Deaf or blind? A Republican or a legless dog? At any moment it may become hard to tell which of these I had been.

It seemed wise to be able to exit with little notice, so at the toddler-size opening of the Nu-lite I unzipped the mosquito net and assumed the posture of a runner in the starting blocks and there remained. The entirety of my plan to save myself boiled down to this and I managed to be smug about it. Now I know why runners don't doze off waiting for the starting gun. Too many elephants. Way too many. It was my fervent wish that no new visitors would disturb my raucous guests.

Longer than the Nile, such a night develops a life of its own (this gave me a total of three lives so I should be grateful). I found it impossible and undesirable at any rate to dwell constantly on my impending doom, thinking how funny to be dead in the morning instead of alive like I usually am and wouldn't it be a kicker if my teachers weren't kidding and I actually go to Hell, and other stuff like that.

"So what flights of fancy did your thoughts take?" you might ask. "What glorious images did the writer conjure with the last hurrah of his consciousness on Earth?" I will tell you. A wide vision, at once flat and round danced giddily before my mind's eye, lavishly blessed with mushrooms, pepperoni, sausage, onions and extra cheese. Yes, I put myself at Sorrento's on Primrose Avenue, a family place where every employee would at some point plop down at your table; where I held the one-sitting calzone-eating record, where the owner's chubby son Dominic would request me to belch for the patrons and I always obliged gloriously, engraving me on his mother's shit-list, and where you could find old Italian songs on the jukebox and get up there and dance to them. I was in the glow of cozy lighting and the friendly chatter of familiar folks in grimy white aprons, seated behind the greatest piping hot pizza they ever made. From my cute little tent pitched in a herd of elephants in the middle of Africa all alone in the dark I told myself, "I will be back there some day and I will have that pizza. I hope."

Sometime in The Night of a Thousand Deaths I detected the approaching swish, swish, krinkle-crackle thud of an expansive Puerto Rican gal in skin-tight jeans striding out of Walmart with six bags of Cheetos and a carton of Diet Coke. Stationing my left eye as close as I dared to the tent flap, I tried to peer around the left corner to espy what could be mimicking this sound. (Yes, I know - the right eye would have been more stealthy but in my case that one is mostly along for the ride.) If indeed it was this shopper leaving Walmart then all bets were off anyway.

A slightly less ominous shape materialized in the foggy gloom, like an elephant with legs and trunk filched by a shoplifting heretic. Then I was hoping for harmony between elephants and hippos, this new peril having accompanied the fog up from the river (I'd like to point out that I've never had this problem before when I went camping). I had been warned that hippos are extremely dangerous under certain conditions but just then they were a bit small to frighten me directly. The idea, though, of an elephant-hippo battle over my campsite did not warm me. I was relieved to see it was all copacetic. I suppose they knew each other. Maybe Dumbo had invited them up to view their project, hoping to get lucky. The hipposterous beings just filed on by and were absorbed back into the fog, trusting the elephants had the situation well in hand. Hip hippo hurray!

At last elephants tired of being tiresome and moved on,

perhaps in search of someone else to scare the broccoli out of. It looked like I had won another day and I reckoned I had earned myself a good night's temporary sleep and lay back down. Apparently the only game in town, after this intermission I heard again untoward sounds and the rude brood returned. I was astounded that there were limbs yet to pull off the tree to haze me with. This was very disappointing and I calculated at this rate I probably would catch the dreaded elephantitis.

I resumed escape posture where it occurred to me that, ironically, I could wind up flat and banal as a cheese pizza. But again they left me inflated, inviting back relief and happiness. A clever man might have scoped a pattern and sought refuge with the rangers; but then a clever man probably wouldn't find himself needing to. As for me I thought surely they'd gone for good and it would be silly (and embarrassing) to go bother a ranger now. As before, I heard trumpeting in the distance. Then I heard it closer but this time it was Louis Armstrong and Elephantsgerald. How delightful that they had strolled up. “Trumpeting? I'll show you trumpeting,” Satchmo growls through that face-erasing grimace and proceeds to horrify every pachyderm for three miles. (Yes, that's right. Not an original thought in my head. I was going to expand that to all the park animals dancing around and who knows where it might have gone from there but then I realized it's all from The Jungle Book.) Good thing for cartoons or I wouldn't have any ideas at all. The nightmare recurred. Close to dawn they really did go home and I fell asleep, not in the starting blocks.

Imagine one minute with this brand of insomnia and then expand that feeling to at least sixty of those every hour all night. Back to back. Used to expecting to be molded like Play-Doh, I had the marvelous feeling of being surprised to wake up, truly a compelling way to start any day. I emerged fearlessly from my tent into a total swamp of splintered tree limbs and elephant shit-piss. It was glorious.

Whether they thought it a hat or a tiny pachyderm in a python, the elephants went to some pains not to disturb my tent though it was hard to tell at the time. I would love to know the role it played in that episode, if the tent fascinated the giants, causing them to keep returning and what they were thinking about it. Maybe they were passive-aggressive, guessing the tree had attracted the tent and destroying the tree to get rid of the tent. And if an elephant truly never forgets, wouldn't it be something if it still lives in some elephant brains out there? Maybe becoming a legend.

Mon. Aug 31

Awake surrounded by elephant shit – breakfast with warden – more never before eaten food – ride to gate – soldiers drunk – one gets rough with warden's men, starts to get rough with warden – heads for hut – soldiers with rifle bar the door – knock him down – various fist fights break out with the guy – finally hog tied and thrown in back of semi and locked up – result of waragi and smoking bangi – warden tells me confidentially that the officer is gone to Lore.

Prime minister and vice president's wife arriving today – here to get things shipshape – they must be expecting a coupe – minister of foreign affairs was here 2 days ago – made stink about rooms. He should try camping. I proceed to Gulu with Warden Akena's aid – (Note – Akena exile for three years, on Amin's death list – all animals killed during this time) – get room at St. Luke's – soldier calls me from truck - give back room – hop on truck full of people – make 100 stops to load stuff - truck takes me to another truck going to Paraa – incredible luck – rangers had brought poachers to court - 1st I think truck is worst thing I could have done – now it's best – kid refuses payment – (200 sh) for 1st ride – says I need money for my travels - Ride to Paraa – see mother lion and 2 cubs in road. Later see 3 more female lions – won't relinquish road – ranger gives me new fruit – mlapear? From gate I ride in cab – ranger asks many questions – pitch tent to the sound of elephants munching trees in the background

Tues. Sept. 1

Awake after good sleep, still 3-d, hoping for boat ride – ants in my tent – relocate. See bird with tail 2 x body length.

So ends my diary. Not bad – it lasted thirteen days during which I became familiar with Uganda moonshine more than I ever did the American equivalent. The quality and intensity of waragy vary greatly between batches.

The young man who refused my payment for a ride considered himself a Christian. A Christian in Uganda is a curious thing. He is what a Christian in more civilized places purports to be.

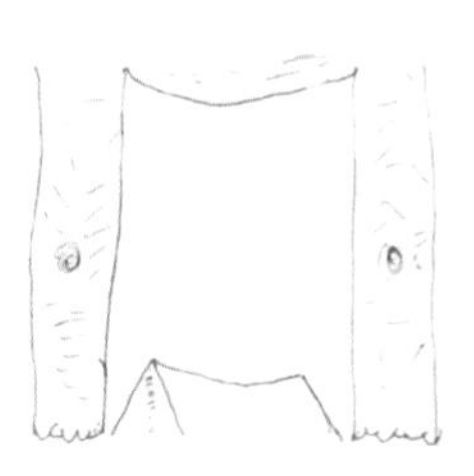

Paraa Sector – Kabalega Falls National Park

Here's a riddle: What do elephants and lightning have in common? In Paraa sector I pitched my tent a bit circumspectly, as in Chobe sector near the rangers' quarters but not under a tree. This put the Nile too far for fishing to be practical so I was totally dependent on the rangers for my meals, a circumstance I didn't relish; showed me what it's like being a pet. But they were gracious hosts and I didn't miss a meal, though I never knew who would be bringing me home next.

While the rangers of Chobe seemed on the silly side, those of Paraa did not. The captain of the rangers, Joseph Lobuinyetu, drilled his men every day so they were fit and well disciplined. It was here that I bitterly regretted the absence of my trusty Humphrey Flyer. Instead of just running up and down for exercise, they could have had such fun with it. Probably they never had seen a frisbee. I would have had to leave it to a worthy new fate.

Joseph and I had lots of quality time leaning our chairs against his hut, listening to African pop music on his portable radio and drinking qeiete' (my spelling) made from sesame seeds, I think. I never determined if it was alcoholic or not. Don't remember what we talked about.

24- year old ranger Johnny Kabagambe took a special interest in me, to my initial dismay. His invitation to breakfast featured dry casava and nothing else. In trying to eat enough to avert insulting him and his wife, I nearly choked to death or died of despair. I can't remember which. But I felt glad when it was over and proud for succeeding, hoping the like of that would never repeat. That afternoon dread overtook reality and Mr. Kabagambe invited me to dinner. To endure it again and survive felt beyond my powers. One likes to be excited about satisfying hunger when he has done little else all day but accrue it. Instead, with leaden heart I contemplated my fate. "What the hell am I doing in Africa anyway? How much more abuse am I supposed to take?" Such were my thoughts. "Why couldn't my great buddy Joseph have invited me?"

African men often hold hands. As Mr. Kabagambe and I strolled from my campsite to his place, in his jubilation he took mine in his. This custom, of all things, I could not abide, especially in my present state of mind. If we hadn't been strolling across a field like Julie Andrews and Christopher Plummer, maybe, but I felt so silly, don't really know exactly why but no doubt a character flaw. So I slipped my hand from his and put it on his shoulder.

But this time it was great. Apparently breakfast had been a practical joke. And Johnny was very excited about a special surprise he had in store for me: My last hot shower or bath had long since faded from memory. This I craved above all else but viewed it as a lost horizon. Not so distant after all, Johnny and his wife had spent some hours boiling over a fire a large tub of water that I might enjoy a luxury I guessed they rarely afforded themselves due to time and firewood consumed – a hot sponge bath. Yeah, this was exactly what the hell I was doing in Africa.

Johnny had a book written in English all about nice ways to behave toward one's fellow man. This was his guide for living.

One day as Joseph and I sat with our quiete', a large male elephant with a small one entered the area. I scooted to my tent for my camera and the big one went for me. Joseph courageously ran between us waving his arms and tried to scare him off. He stopped it but the elephant never really backed down or mellowed out.

Having been acquainted only with personable elephants, this surprised me. Joseph was familiar with these two and the belligerence of the big one. He explained that the small one had no family and in an unusual move, the large male had adopted him. One can easily imagine the big male had ample cause to hate people, maybe lighter skinned ones particularly.

Joseph told me about an elephant that had purposely destroyed a tent. During the tree party, I drew some serenity from an account I had just read portraying elephants as reasonable folk. Had I heard Joseph's story instead, the night would have been even longer.

Johnny Kabagambe was determined to teach me Swahili. Thanks to him I still can ask someone where the road goes, (badda badda he, ne quenda wappi) inquire of him his name (jeeni lanco nanni) and give him mine (jeeni longo Einstein).

The rangers wished me to see the waterfall. I didn't care all that much, having been to North Carolina and seen a couple waterfalls. Still they thought it would be a terrible shame to miss this one so I humored them. The park had a boat apparently modeled after the African Queen but a deal less magnificent. Years prior, in another world, it had carried tourists to the falls. The rangers vowed to fire her up for me if I would cover the cost of the excursion, thirty-five hundred shillings; equivalent to forty-six dollars to them, fourteen to me thanks to the black market. That was all my Uganda shillings but I agreed. The day I was to go, the warden of Paraa drove up to me in his Land Rover, shook my hand and said "I do not want you to be without money, so you will go for eighteen hundred." That might have covered the kerosene.

A couple rangers' wives got on board the Momba (Swahili for crocodile), very excited, apparently going upriver for the first time. I climbed up and sat cross legged on the front end of the roof and had one of the most unforgettable experiences of my life.

I'm going to stretch myself to the limit to bring you to what's coming but even if I over-write it, my words alone will leave the story undertold. This is one of those places where the reader has to pitch in. Remember, there's only one first time and this may be as close as you're going to come to Kabalega Falls. Don't squander it.

Go slow, don't move to the next line until you've absorbed the current one. Let your imagination run riot with it and you feel you are there, cross legged or standing on the roof, with nothing in your life to hint at what awaits you except ominous clues now coming your way. At least triple the magnitude of everything I wrote. Take what you know of sound and spectacle and let them swell beyond belief. Take your time. Feel the wonder, the magnitude that we humans, tiny and crushable as we are, are capable of absorbing...

The women waved good-bye as Momba pushed her nose into the current. We plowed steadily up the churning White Nile, hippos and crocs lining the shore, the croc mouths stuck open waiting, I supposed, for something delicious and stupid to stroll in. We pulled alongside one crocodile so long I had to switch to wide angle lens to get most of its body. And this from the roof. We were fighting our way up the raging tumult that is the new-born Nile, surrounded by far-off hills and lush green jungle. It would have looked like this before mankind was here to confirm it, with only the mechanical boat and the camera in my hand to tell me anything had changed.

An hour before we came in sight of Kabalega Falls, which I have since read is driven by the strongest water pressure on the face of Earth, a murmur reached my ears. As Momba pushed her bow further up the swirling drink of Africa, the phenomenon ahead grew from murmur to a rumor of thunder and as the rumor became undeniable and then a wild proclamation of disaster, my anticipation grew to obsession.

Mist appeared with no visible source. As we progressed, I stood, out of respect or primal fear of whatever this battering of my senses could mean and joy that such was possible and I would survive it. It had long been impossible to speak or hear anything else. One thing for sure, something was going on up there of an entirely different order than North Carolina.

An omnipresent, thunderous roar like five hundred sphinx-size lions annihilated any other attempt at audio; the air was solid with it and could hold no more, like the impenetrable flood of sound crammed into the space was holding us off. As strange as this reads, it was a little surprising we could see through it. Voices jammed down our throats, thoughts pounded out of our consciousness, we negotiated a sharp bend in the Nile now defined by towering palisades on both sides. As the cliff on the right moved out the way, the source of this overload slid into view, dominating the horizon, a war of water against planet. Ancient, all powerful, the barrier of the Lost World, an avalanche of turquoise catastrophe blasted a rift in the jungle like life itself bursting from the primordial ooze.

The Momba strained onward but finally stopped for safety way short of where I wanted to be. We were holding our own against Kabalega wind, Nile flow and cacaphony on a whirlpool-whipped lagoon and I imagined the giant Nile perch, which get hundreds of pounds, below us.

If disappointment can crown ecstasy than that is how I felt. The trip back wasn't nearly long enough. My idea of this planet's potential blown to atoms through no design of my own, it frightened me to think of all the other unsuspected wonders I was liable to miss.

That's how the boat ride seemed to me. Back on shore I bade a sad good-bye to Joseph and Johnny who seemed true friends though we'd known each other briefly. I left the magical land of the park thinking I might check out the fishing in Zaire next, as long as I was out and about.

Ugandans kept doing nice things for me just to do a kindness. They were extremely nice people and hopefully it was rubbing off on me. Of course when people are nice to you, you feel like passing that on. The system is self perpetuating because you always feel like being nice. I incurred a lifelong debt in Uganda, one that is pleasant to pay back. I'm still not very nice but I am improved.

anoffday

The bus from Hoima to Fort Portal had been stopped frequently, three times running at intervals of no more than a hundred yards. Each time everyone exited the bus and lined up and it was getting tedious. Probably the bandits didn't expect me to get out but in solidarity with the others I always did so after hiding my camera. The purpose of these rituals was to rob the passengers but I never saw money exchanging hands. Perhaps my confounding presence in line inhibited that.

At the last stop a wooden pole across the road was the symbolic barrier. The only hold-up where I witnessed violence, it appeared to be an overzealous get-out-the-vote drive. Here a sixteen year old boy accused of not having a voter identification card was slapped around in front of us all including an off - duty policeman en route to his first vacation in five years. I got the feeling he didn't want anything to rock that boat. The policeman's entreaties were futile. "They don't speak our language," he told me. I didn't know if he meant figuratively or actually, as many Sudanese were turning up in the uniform of the Uganda Army. (About this time President Obote issued an edict prohibiting impersonation of a Uganda soldier.) The boy was then escorted into the bushes by the tall, inhuman officer for further abuse, of what nature I don't know, perhaps a civics lesson. The policeman would not be seen again until we reboarded.

This was a long stop but finally I was granted passage to the other side of the "roadblock." Lacking the imagination of my fellow passengers, I ruined the illusion that the road actually was blocked, by taking the shortcut and stepping over their pole. That sparked the following question and answer session between me and the only soldier who spoke English and who was very proud of his facility with it:

"What is that?" he fumed, pointing to the "roadblock."

Oh, I know this one, I thought. "A stick."

But he was looking for something more. "What kind of stick is it?" the soldier asked with heightened belligerence.

Not prepared for his interest in botany, I was unable to "Name the tree." "A stick in the road," I elaborated with a commensurate rise in flippancy. (Flippancy is a personality disorder that comes with the "smart mouth," developed for elementary school teachers and difficult to stifle on a moment's notice.)

Of course Machine Gun Bob Barker was angling for "It's a roadblock."

The host was a little shit but he was holding a pretty dangerous looking appliance. I said, "You could shoot your eye out."

No, I didn't really say that. That's in the "wish I had said" category, so I could tell people I said that. I don't think he would have gotten it.

In an increased state of agitation (I've been told I can have this effect on people) he asked me what was the ***purpose*** of the stick. I supplied the correct answer and then to show I could do it right, I stepped back over it, then walked around. I think that was pretty funny but it went over with this humorless sod like a lead cannibal.

It was The Little Stick that Could. Could be a real roadblock if it just tried hard enough and didn't give up. He loved his little stick and he was so proud of it, lying there trying so hard.

He blurted, "I could kill you for that," at which point I twigged how emotionally invested he was.

Well that tears it – finally someone threatening to personally kill me. I shouldn't be so surprised. The black buffalo of my acquaintance held the power of life or death over me, and that I could and did live with; but not this twerp. I told myself it must be me, not him who decides my fate. Best if I'd just stayed in the bus.

I viewed with heightened interest the position of the gun, not yet pointed at me and therefore incapable of harm, feeling if that started to change, I must grab it or greet a friend and attack when he turns around to look (both responses to someone "getting the drop on you" gleaned from my other mentor, The Lone Ranger, whom I wouldn't have minded seeing about then). That would give 'em a start, wouldn't it, teach 'em to mess with an American. They'd surely never seen a Western or maybe even a tv and here comes this colonial super-hero rearing up on a zebra whiter than he is yellin' High yo Silver, pearl handled revolvers and silver bullets, masked and shooting their weapons out their hands. Well, it's a nice fantasy, wrong continent.

I was disappointed at the fruit my bus ride was rotting into because I think I'm funny, something like I had originally intended to avoid by avoiding Uganda. Getting, in my opinion, way too big for his britches, my antagonist went on to boast, "I could even kill Milton Obote, the President of Uganda for doing that." Uncle Milty would have been very interested to hear that. Always room for one more in the mass graveyard.

My recall of the scene starts to fade at this point. I may have responded with, "You're pretty strict. It wouldn't even get him impeached where I come from."

The rest is a blank. Who knows what other hilarious pokes I probably took at him before he shot me. I'll admit I'm tempted to make up some more witty stuff I might have said and then more stupid stuff he would have said and insert it to enhance the reader's enjoyment. Sometimes I regret this is a truthful narrative.

So – even better, now the reader writes the book – extend the scene as long as you like. There you are on the road, bus pulled over, African scrub all around, passengers standing in obedience to a pole in the road manned by a handful of slobbering dolts in army fatigues. Given that you're feeling pretty flippant, needle the guy. Whip out the sarcasm. He's asking for it with that last line. We've nothing to lose now. Take more space if you need it....

Phew! He didn't kill us but little thanks to you for that. Christ! I said "flippant," not suicidal. Well, I've always been a bad influence on people. Now that we're back on the bus in one piece, I gotta say, some of it was classic. "That's not a roadblock. It's not even a toadblock." You hurt him with that. But when you said, "You better shoot your Mama now 'cause she's too fat to get around the stick?" OOOwee! Ouch! He had nothin' to come back with but hot lead. Good thing I had my Uganda High Commission paper handy.

Maybe someday he'll get himself a real roadblock and calm down. But I doubt it.

Most public transportation, if doubtful of arriving before dark, would camp along the way rather than risk a roadblock at night when the soldiers would not be intoxicated only by power. Due to the delays our last leg was in the dark, undertaken with misgivings. There were no further incidents and the bus made it to Fort Portal. A passenger in his twenties, Charles Ntegyereize appointed himself my guardian. The policeman volunteered also but Charles offered first so I went with him. Had I gone with the policeman, a certain event may have passed without my knowledge; while a learning experience, not one I cherish. Charles escorted me to a small restaurant.

I was spooning into my supper when a commotion in the street drew everyone to the window. It consisted of five army officers and one small citizen. I'm not brave, just sometimes inflexible, unwilling to suffer disagreeable events and confident in the ability of malefactors to see it my way. Never one to abide unequal combat, I was out the door and heading for the fray.

Halfway there I saw the man make a break but grabbed and heaved into the back of a pick-up truck. I then noticed with surprise that I was not leading the charge. I was the charge. Slower to answer the call, the others were still in the restaurant. When I looked back, all motioned me to return as if creating an air current to accomplish it. I counter-waved but they didn't fall for it. (Where's Chester and Wayne when you need them?) I returned to see what they wanted and why they were still there. They wanted me back inside; so I came in and urged them to sally forth but they were not of a mind to be inspired. Their resigned faces showed exasperation. "This is what Uganda is," explained one man in his lilting accent, "You can be killed at any time."

Still, ganging up on a guy is a clear code violation and I pressed them from my position of newcomer. "You'd better tell your friend how it is in Uganda," Charles was warned as if I were his fault. They said it was lucky the soldiers hadn't seen me, and going back out might draw fatal attention to the restaurant. "Even the color of your skin could be enough to make them want to kill you," someone said, "and once they want to kill you, they don't stop."

Here's a moral dilemma I didn't anticipate. With all the contingencies I had prepared for - would I rather be a possum or an armadillo, have pizza or sex, burn or freeze to death, again I'm on new ground. I'll bet you're wondering if I'd lose Beethoven or Tchaikovsky. I can tell you this – the only thing keeping old Ludwig in there is the Ninth Symphony. So what goes through your mind? What would John Wayne do? He'd probably ask Ronald Reagan. Given time for such reflection I thought, "It's not my country anyway. His own countrymen aren't willing to help him. I'm a damn tourist. What business is it of mine?" Well, I felt the burden of kindness shown me in Uganda and it seemed like it was my business.

We already know I don't see the big picture. Maybe people don't fear death when we should because we never actually learn we can get killed, being something that happens at most once. How can we truly believe in a state that exists only when we are no longer capable of believing? Without the "Wow! That sucked, think I'll play it safe from now on" moment. We've seen others die but the whole idea of our own untimely demise beggars the imagination.

As would most people with the luxury of outrage, I believed this must be stopped. Though belief should be unwavering, I was considering a new normal. I thought about home and people I dearly wanted to see me again. And I figured that man had a family. But the refusal of the others indicated potential for regret. Were they over- cautious or just experienced? I even the odds to five against two to better suit my notions and if things go badly, with plenty of pages left and absurd as it may seem, my passport gets its final stamp.

It hadn't sunk in that they were killing him. That was a few too many for me and may have worked in my favor. At a certain point *Webster's New Dictionary for the Illiterate* definition of "enough" comes into play, as in enough is enuff. Comprehending the goal, the loose cannon probably would have rolled back out, consensus be durned. And I might have probably bluffed them with my white self, producing my paper from the Uganda High Commission and clearing the street. Five though is a lot of guys to fool, especially if they're intoxicated enough to just not give a lion fart.

Anyway, I had been warned I could jeopardize the other diners and advised to butt out. I should not presume to know better than locals, who liked it no more than I did. Maybe the poor schmuck should have had the sense to stay out the bar. Time to stop making people nervous and sit back down.

It was a long game of cats and mouse with many spoonfuls of lentil soup interrupted by the sounds. While I still looked, before settling back to my meal, they would allow him to escape, running to the fuzzy border of the dismal light from the lone street lamp only to be caught and returned to the not okay corral, watched by sympathetic people who would not intervene. So near yet so terribly far. We might as well have cheered them on. I think the other diners didn't know him. I wonder if that would have made a difference.

As my bowl's interior inexorably emerged, I could tell a particularly effective blow had landed not by the victim's groans but by those of the men still watching at the window. They recoiled almost as if hit themselves. In these moments my appetite would demur and the spoon suspend where it was. There were no words spoken by the victim, no calls for help, no attempt at reasoning with his tormentors. Maybe the talking had occurred earlier.

Charles wished to get away at once but I was hungry and insisted on finishing my meal. Though increasingly anxious, he stayed with me. Leaving a few beans in my bowl, we slipped through shadows to his brother's apartment where one of us slept on the floor and both with the wish that should the soldiers require a nightcap as Charles said they often did, our place would not be visited; and yes, in so doing, wishing it on others. Lying down in the dark had drained my belligerence, the big picture seeped in and finally I felt afraid.

As we lay there, Charles explained they were not just beating the man up. For fun they took him outside to make him die way sooner than he thought he would, opposite a doctor's impulse; wiping out the joys and sorrows of living, remembered and to come. That was power. And it was officers, widely considered the hope of the army, drinking in the bar next door as was this small fellow with the terrible timing. I don't know what was their excuse or if they needed one. Charles said the canceled life would be found the next day in a ditch.

Yep, a frustrating finish to this episode because I gave up the dice and raked in my safe outcome. At this writing I, like the reader, kind of wish I had pushed it, just to know if the universe was prepared to let me pull it off with no harm. I feel like it was. Mom used to credit St. Jude with good works. Maybe he would have thrown in. Anyway there was more on the line than I knew – two fine young men I eventually sired, maybe save the world some day, at the very least have some fun in it; a shame to lose them after they managed to survive Chobe. There's those unforeseeable consequences again; but maybe events work in the opposite direction and I continued because their existence in the grand scheme of things required mine. Burdened with prescience of their possible arrival, would my path would have been clearer? This illuminates the difficulty in making intelligent decisions: of the dimensions past, present and future, we're allowed knowledge only of the two we've already screwed up.

After that night I was feeling less satisfied with Number One, having learned that a code of behavior and that code put to the test can be different things and substituting a convenient new standard cannot but take a bite out of you. Placing a premium on one's life, I found, devalues it, regardless of the circumstances; like checking your credit score I suppose; although maybe it was just the old survival instinct catching up again. I was feeling sour about the whole trip just then, missing the innocent days of Lake Turkana and my little pal Agostino. Better equipped there, I'd still have been walking around the amazing lake, maybe having a tiger fish lunch with my friend Swalik.

Fort Portal was just the place to pick up a nice little straw Uganda shopping basket so I got one and headed out of town to Kasese.

In Kasese I called on the police station and asked to sleep there. I had a couple beers with two policemen, one of whom reviled me repeatedly for pants too short. I found his Victorianism tiresome and ironic and pointed out, "Why are you worried about my shorts? A generation back or two your whole family was probably running around naked." Which left him without much else to say. Then I went to bed in the back of one of their vehicles. I was awakened in the night about a thousand times by one thing or another.

Kasese produced a young fellow named Abu Bashir Baker. He proclaimed himself a "sportsman" which means he loved sports and didn't drink alcohol or smoke. Soccer is popular in Uganda and I was invited to play with him and his friends. It happens I love to play soccer and am always on the lookout for a game.

Yahoo! We ran barefoot the dirt road through town herding the ball to the playing field, another moment when I marveled at my prosperity. There was nothing I'd rather have been doing, including fishing. We had a great game highlighted by a terrific goal. One of my teammates and I hit it off especially well and we set it up together, me heading in his perfect lob. I'm sure everyone playing that day remembers it as clearly as I do.

Abu owned a pocket-size Berlitz *Swahili for Travelers* which I coveted earnestly. He traded it for photographing him in his soccer finery and sending the print. Everyone in Uganda changed into their best duds for a photo. I never expected them to have such clothes on hand and the reappearance was magical, like Superman stepping back out the phone booth. Holding the ball overhead, he leaped sideways in the air and we faked a stop-action of him making a great save as goalie. Turned out perfect and I sent him a framed 5 x 8.

I was stuck between heading straight to Tanzania or first visiting Zaire. Zaire looked tantalizing on the map, huge and wild, probably lots of crazy fish. I acquiesced to the universe's whim. My first ride was a bus going toward Zaire.

Like hopeful kids with a lemonade stand, along the way some uniformed bandits were set up for business and as usual, they went unchallenged. One got on the roof of the bus and started to open my pack; so, having learned nothing at the previous roadblock, and without a blueprint for success, I climbed up too. Once up there I had the idea to draw again on elementary school skills; so I mimicked him with monkey faces and scratching and stuff which was a hit with everyone including his cohorts on the ground. Humiliated, he climbed down and, nearing the finish line, I still had everything.

This brings to mind another fine adage – "Laughter is the best medicine." The episode revealed to me my natural Jewish comedic talents which had lacked the right audience before and I considered taking that show on the road back home, though unsure how it would be received. I'd probably have to add a few more hilarious impersonations.

My next ride was more or less a pickup truck; and it was a mutatu, incredibly weighed down with Ugandans, chickens and goats. No mutatu in Uganda had the insane luxury of a battery. It was one of those items not absolutely necessary that fade out of the general consciousness and get replaced by skills peculiar to the deficit such as push starting. I suppose by now they have reinvented the crank. More interesting was the real or imagined ability to wring the last inch out of a drop of gas. Typically they killed the engine and coasted downhill in neutral. But this driver was fanatic. Once having push - started his car, he was body and soul attuned to every rise and dip in the road, pouncing on each infinitesimal opportunity to coast and knowing precisely when to pop the clutch and re-engage. In a total downhill of course that will save gas but I never was convinced the neurotic off and on in the nearly level stretches was any more than a man trying futilely to affect his fate. Wearing out the clutch might eventually cancel the saved gas money but maybe that was too far down the road to matter.

For once I was in a little hurry, hoping to reach a town before night and this guy was turning off the car on what appeared to be level stretches of road and coasting. I said the thing was incredibly full when I got on. It got incredibler. We stopped for every chicken, goat, sack of grain and Ugandan in the world and sucked it in. About dark the monstrously overburdened machine, springs pressed flat, heroically rolled into some town and disgorged itself.

Next day I reached the little Shangrilah (though I didn't know it yet) Mbwera on the frontier of Zaire. I skipped Mbwera and hopped on a truck headed on a red clay road the final four miles to the border. I was surprised by rich looking fertile countryside broken up now and then by a (ugh) casava garden or a lovely straw and bamboo house. We passed a truck and I was shocked to see standing in the back the first mzungu since leaving Kampala with the exception of the UN Dutch guy. He was coming from Zaire where I was heading and I was coming from where he was going. How I ached to commiserate but our timing was off by minutes. Our gazes locked as we drew apart. From his face on seeing me, I knew he was feeling the same thing. We were like dogs on the street dying to interact pulled opposite ways by their leashes.

I had read in *Africa on the Cheap* that Zaire did not require a visa. Of course these things are subject to change. Before long I was having a nice stroll back down that same lovely road returning to Mbwera. Had I stopped in Mbwera before heading toward Zaire, we tourists would have met and he would have become a more memorable part of my trip. Had I made it into Zaire, that may have become the trip, pretty vast place, I might still be there. Instead, just a name on the map with no faces, no magic video in my head to make it real.

I took a room in Mbwera and began enjoying my stay in this relaxed little town engulfed by banana trees as far as the eye could see. Lake Edward also was visible far in the distance. I found out the white fellow was Canadian. He had stayed a few hours, just long enough to make a common thing out of me. And then left. The effect was only temporary. I still was quite a novelty and he soon was forgotten. I remember him as I do Zaire: a land glimpsed but never visited.

By sheer providence I had arrived in black Mayberry. Notice the similarity in the names. The folks were exceedingly open and friendly with little impinging on their time. Visitors usually passed through between countries and my stay there confounded them. One day while walking along a banana tree lined path (what other kind was there?) I sat under a tree. A nearby family became concerned. Finally they left their house and walked over like a committee to inquire of my well being. Deflecting my lack of need, they were bound to help and so, unable to defuse their alarm, I had to get up and leave.

An affronted twelve year old boy (Barney Fife?) strode out

avidly bellicose and forthright to accuse me of photographing his thatched bamboo house to give my friends back home a good laugh. He would not back down from his premise and accept that I felt only admiration for it, very comfortable looking and natural, not a blot on the land but part of it. It was one too many for him. Maybe I made him feel like a zoo exhibit with no way to know that I had come from the real zoo. I wonder where that extraordinary spirit took him.

That day an old fellow shakily topped a hill on the path and coasted down to me on a Raleigh bicycle purchased by his grandfather in 1920. It had endured without repair except a peddle had decayed a little. Never has a circumstance cried out louder for a particular adage, so I will state it. When the chance comes to write something that even a German school teacher could not refute, then I must take it. Opportunity knocks but once as they say. That was not the adage in mind but it's not a bad one. Here it comes: "They don't make 'em like they used to."

They grow as many types of bananas there as are shades of green in Ireland. The only ones considered edible straight out the skin are these short fat unspeakably delicious ones. The kind we value in the U.S. are looked upon there as we look upon plantains. In fact they know about a hundred jillion ways to cook the yellow herb so they get carried away and in Mbwera you never stop eating them (Herein lies the essential difference between humans and apes. While apes are contemplating the universe, we devote time and thought to how we eat bananas). Their version of mashed potatoes is matoke and it appears with every meal. This perpetually renewed parade of bananas through me demented my digestion. I became a walking calliope of rumbles, gurgles, upheavals and gaseous expulsions that made me a bit anxious.

Otherwise I led an idyllic existence in Mbwera, stepping away from the avalanche for a few days vacation from my vacation. I loitered around town with my innards bubbling over, getting to know everybody and drinking weird bottled soda, going down the Zaire road to fish or bathe in the stream. Sometimes I gave fish to kids watching me, fascinated that I could pull them out like that. The fish were small so I was using tiny squirrel tail jigs. My rod and reel were admired like a magic wand. I bathed one day with two truck drivers who had stopped to lather up in my tub. The big amber bars of soap used there look like what I had known as saddle soap.

Many pleasant interludes passed in conversation with local customs officials. These men were eager to discover if they knew some things about the fairer sex that American men do not. I could have blown their minds with tales of the triple buttocked Congresswomen of the Mississippi Delta and some such but I went easy.

One afternoon as we lounged by the road chewing the fat, a very stern and strong-looking woman (Nope. This ain't Aunt Bea) whom I had noticed eyeing me while I was fishing, stopped and asked in front of everybody, "Would you like me to accommodate you?" I felt on the spot like a woman whose boyfriend proposes at a party with all his friends. She looked a bit tough for my taste, like a new automobile tire or something, so to spare her public humiliation, I agreed to meet at the Friday night dance in a couple days. Where I had been eagerly anticipating this event, I viewed it now with a degree of dread. As appointments will, mine arrived. I got there a bit late and we didn't find each other. Perhaps she'd cooled off and forgotten.

The generally open attitude may have facilitated the coming rapid spread of AIDS through Uganda. One fellow already was talking about fixing me up with one of his girlfriends and I was told, "If you stay around for a couple of weeks, you will really find out how we live."

This somewhat remote village apparently had done the time without the crime, untouched by the violence since the advent of Amin. Said one local shrugging happily, "We can't believe we are in Uganda." There was even a pleasant soldier around town. I was sorely tempted to stay and find out how they really lived because it seemed the lesson would include many pleasant recesses. But one day the weather gloomed up, a truck was passing through and I hopped on. This is a flaw in having infinite places to go. The call of the open road is strong and you tend to leave prematurely, never diving below the surface.

There also was a time component, my Rwanda visa nearing extinction. I needed to start heading that way or risk returning to Kampala for a renewal, a place I hoped to keep in the "been there done that" bin. That I still was less than three weeks out of Kampala was astounding. Next stop - Kabale, where my new traveling partner awaited me.

As I walked into town on the main street, an enthusiastic customs official ran out into the road to meet me. "So," I thought, "*This* is how Elvis feels." Though Ugandan she had kind of the angular face of a Rwandan but I didn't realize that yet. And she aimed to please. A fine representative of the government, first off she told me a man to change money with. That led to a funny incident. Right after selling him some dollars, I went to the police office to leave my pack while I walked around. I later learned the poor guy thought I was turning him in and he lit out of town.

Then she showed me around. We lunched at a restaurant where I was served something memorable. First they brought me a piece of meat too tough to cut. So my guide said, "You want soft meat?"

"Yes," I replied, "that's what I want," picturing a tenderized steak.

They brought me Cthulhu's baby sister in a bowl. It appeared to have suction cups all over it but it wasn't a cephalopod. Not a cephalopod but suction cups – not a good look. I knew only it was disgusting. Turned out to be something's stomach. I turned that down too and regretted that already I was getting known as a picky eater.

"What does the guy want???" they probably were thinking.

"Hey," I might have said, "Don't you have any o' them good ol' black eyed peas? I'd sure eat some o' those." And I might have.

Must not have been much doing at the office because next we visited some half-caste friends of hers. She said half-castes are exalted as special people (unlike the "breeds" of American Westerns). We perused photo albums. Later in a bar I would meet a half-caste man I recognized from the albums, which was a strange feeling. Pre-internet, people you saw in photography before phlesh usually were celebrities. Made him like a celebrity. I was not accustomed to meeting cosmopolitan Africans and stranger yet he'd been to San Francisco. Finally my guide visited me in my motel room of a thousand and one holes and helped me kill mosquitoes all night.

We plugged a hole and then executed each and every mosquito in the room. This was our excruciating method. We were sure we had plugged *the* hole; but quicker than you can say Milton Obote ten times the room was full like the tiny wrecked vampires had simply re-inflated with blood lust. The search was on again for what we optimistically dubbed the *other* hole. We found it and plugged it and killed all the mosquitoes in the room again. As if the room had a mosquito capacity that must be maintained, the next shift was outside waiting for us to finish. Out with the old mosquitoes... Soon the room was lavishly restocked. We twigged the game and targeted a new quarry far tougher than the first two. With grim determination we hunted the *last* hole.

The last hole eluded us. Would that we could have found it right off the bat and saved the first hole for last, where it wouldn't matter. But that seems never to be how the universe operates.

Time was, a dollar and a half meant something. That room must have been their "malaria special." On the educational side it gave me some idea how it was for the American Indians. They thought they killed us all and the next minute, "Heeeere's Johnny!"

Next day I saw something very unusual indeed: a paleface.

This one was pale as a bucket, a long, blonde, bow legged young stick of German Doublemint in billowing blue pants – my new conscience, Eckaru Wallis.

It seems the blast furnaces of Germany forge dual tourist models – the typical ones that travel in packs, are obnoxious and arrogant with no justification (look at me– I am uncool, dull, without pigment and we lose all the wars. So I am superior) and believe that wherever they are is Deutchland. Seasoned world traveler that I am now and having encountered a few, I consider myself qualified to make this observation. It matches the popular perception of the only globally despised tourist wherever he has gone. Explained a Spanish waiter the previous summer in Toledo: "Americans and Germans are both loud and boisterous. But with the Americans it is in a nice way."

The anomalous group, represented by Eckaru, travel without a gang, are unassuming and go to extremes of minimal offense to compensate for the first group. Some, like Irmin Opper step off the conveyor belt with impurities, neither entirely one nor the other. When I told Eckaru of Irmin's alcohol-handshake trick, he railed, "Germans like that should not go anywhere. They should just stay home." Eckaru was something of a rebellious kid anyway, by his accounts of his life in Germany.

For someone to expose the petty scale of my personal complaints, there was reason to look no further. I'd heard accounts of tough passages through Sudan – lost, drinking from the radiator, all resolved happily; but Eckaru's would prove a balm for my soul. It seems sure that he was a jinx so could not have escaped it. As this saga begins, he is with a group of friends:

We find them at the bottom of Egypt en route to Tanzania via Sudan and then the lush, cool Uganda. Their immediate goal is Wadihalfa at the top of Sudan, to catch a ferry to Khartoum. There Eckaru and his melaninless companions, including his soon to be former girlfriend, intend to catch a boat to Juba.

Just before reaching Wadihalfa, which boasts daily temperatures well over a hundred and officially the highest sunlight saturation on Earth, Eckaru innocently proposes a little side trip which costs them a day, not realizing that's only the down payment. Soon they will notice this slight aberration in their progress has lent them a new schedule. The vigorous band of German youth, imbued with the joy of forward movement, arrive the next day in Wadihalfa to be told the boat left an hour ago. (So near yet so far, eh? One of the most poignant of German adages.)

Really it broiled down to that hour. And what's an hour normally? For many, barely time for their morning toilette. Too little occurs in an hour to be remembered for very long. Sure, we might remember weeks, even days that hosted a memorable hour; but hours? Sometimes. Pull from their timeline that one measly circuit by the long hand, one twenty-fourth of a day, and all would have been entirely different. And better. Much better. They were not a crowd for making lemonade with lemons. The inflation rate on that hour was exorbitant.

Eckaru and company might have latched onto some sort of camel caravan through the desert or maybe conjured St. Exupery's ghost for an airlift; but being people of faith in schedules, they opted to await the boat's promised return. With the luxury of the big picture, they might have decided otherwise. Maybe just turned around and gone home. But it is the big picture we never get. In its place we have optimism.

Every excruciating day roasting in Wadihalfa is mirror to the one before and the one ahead of it, but the sunburnt counters of these replicas are deteriorating and Eckaru's continued life is becoming a bone of contention. Like an exclamation point, change arrives as hepatitis, occupying most of the group including our hero. Any good feelings for Eckaru that someone might have nursed are rendered a distant if not irretrievable and blasphemous regret.

The reader is rightly thinking any writer worth his salt and pepper would insert at this point an epic Poem of Eckaru. I apologize. I'm trying but nothing is coming and I refuse to just slap something together..... Actually, I simply can't be bothered. I have other things to do besides sitting around writing epic poems. Maybe later...

Two weeks in, an emaciated, blithering German spots a speck on the horizon. “Ach du lieber!” he yells hoarsely like Gabby having spied the new Sheriff of Rock Ridge. “Ach du lieber!”

“Vas did he say?”

“He said der ship is getting bigger!”

Yes, there it is, with unmentionable joy the group spies looming ever larger on the Nile, the fabled floater that is to become their deliverance from nothing to do but roast the other side. Their young, resilient spirits spring to new heights. Perhaps room still beats in their hearts to forgive and rebuild the wretched Eckaru.

But “Nein!” Sprach Zarathustra. There will be no salvaging the pariah. The ferry pulls up to the dock and lack of fuel is poured on their new fire. They are informed that the tank is empty.

“Ach du liber! That's no problemma. When will it be refueled?”

Just then a witch buzzes them on her broomstick cackling, “Never! Never! And your little dog too!”

That may have been Eckaru hallucinating, or me, but maybe not.

“There is no fuel in Wadihalfa,” they were told, “but never fear, it will be here soon.”

Quite right, two weeks later the desiccated, twisted German slag bucket of venom and spite shoehorn themselves into the crammed barge. Affording relief from the reek of urine, low air pressure pulls the black exhaust cloud onto the deck. Thus they irreparably motor upstream out of Wadihalfa, inundated in and ably contributing to every kind of animal filth and stench. That day, nay that hour had become a month during which their funds, their health and the trip of their lives evaporated pointlessly in the desert. They hadn't lived that month. They had lived one blistering day thirty times.

With purpose remaining equal to bodies floating down the Ganges, they dock at Khartoum and gratefully depart the Nasty Nautilus. Now entoumed in Khartoum, they roast for another week, spending many unhappy hours watching the only movie in town. In keeping with Eckaru's luck one would expect it to be *Khartoum*, starring Charlton Heston and Laurence Olivier. As it happens, it is. A week of this at this point seems a monstrous imposition; but the locals, who live it, don't get white man's time or his impatience to be where entertainment isn't watching again the only movie in town. Unaware that there are other movies, they are satisfied.

Able to perform as a troupe the entire film, the tourists press their remains into another crammed ferry to fight the current away from Khartoum. Some days later they find themselves in the longed-for Juba, unclean to their skeletons and unable to recall why it ever had seemed a good place to go. With no further boating opportunities, they clamber hypnotically into the back of some kind of an African truck heading south. Now there's a promising direction, they all must have thought. It sounds like the place we started out going to, so very long ago.

Having dumped his north-bound load there, the driver of that conveyance may well have been waiting for south-bound passengers almost as long as the Germans were in Wadihalfa. He might have arrived an hour or ten minutes late for the ferry, his truckload waiting with him ever since. Maybe he wouldn't start back without a load, didn't know there was no fuel in Wadihalfa, all his passengers wondering why the ferry didn't return: inflation at both ends striking down chronological time.

With experience of these, I picture this new ride with sides and horizontal wood strips fastened to vertical posts around the front and sides of the bed to perch people all the way up, expanding capacity. Employed in the business of carrying, as is everything there that moves, it must maximize the number of fares. The driver never would turn away a customer no matter how solid his load. So much time goes to this that you sincerely wonder if you will get anywhere or if you have stepped into a state of limbo. If a man by the road is transporting his pet rhinoceros and the truck saturated, you will stop and a way will be found for them. Always room for more. Once underway the cargo function as one organism, rebreathing the common air and the flesh contiguous save a cloth membrane preventing osmosis, as united in their direction as the molecules of a missile. Had the driver been the innkeeper, Mary and Joseph would have lain down atop at least one of everything Noah salvaged and then had some layers added on top of them. They'd have staggered away with the wrong baby and Jesus for sure would have been black or maybe not even human. The driver's only frustration stems from the inability for matter to co-occupy the same exact space and he comes pretty close to achieving that. Forget your Hedron Collider. One of these entrepreneurs will be first to violate the laws of nature.

The open bed features a tarp attached at the front to be spread in case of rain. This rolling ark is supernaturally bursting with chickens, goats, four–foot tall burlaps of flour, Sudanese people, women nursing babies, Jesus, meteorites, everything else and squeezed into this, a gaggle of withered young German tourists, no longer optimistic about life but still fostering an embattled belief in the intrinsic fairness of the universe.

According to Eckaru the road is of a character that creates butter from the milk some passengers carry and this is their intention. On and on they churn inexorably through the day as if trying to outdistance an unseen scourge nipping at their heels and then on and blindly on through the opaque night, motion detected only in shifting, bouncing and shaking and now the deluge because the monsoon has caught them, a rainy season the Germans well know had not yet begun a month or even two weeks before. Passengers manage to spread the tarp and tie it, squeezing down the high-riders into the lower protoplasm and everyone wants to stop and sleep, even the sacks of flour sagging from standing all day like mute, disgruntled midgets and the people pound on the back window of the truck cab to make the driven driver stop but he refuses and they continue barreling down the road and now slipping and sliding as well because the mud has churned to teflon, tire tread surrendered and a lunatic at the wheel.

Who knows why he wouldn't stop. He had a cab to wait out the stormy night in dryness. Maybe he was straining to make up time spent festering in Juba where he gambled that he still could beat the rain. Probably he knew the road would only get worse with time. Maybe he dreaded trying to push start the thing in the mud. Or because he was in motion he couldn't stop. One thing he had was momentum – mv. Lotta mass in that m, all dedicated to somewhere ahead, lose the all-important v if he stopped. Maybe he himself was a force of nature. The rain didn't stop, the suffering didn't stop, the outcry didn't stop. Why should his truck stop? Don't wanta be the one thing stationary in that maelstrom. Hand on the jerking shifter knob, lean over the steering wheel, try to see ahead, hope the windscreen wipers hold. At least present a moving target to the slings and arrows of outrageous fortune.

In the mire and misery of the Sudanese rainy season night, German youth mashed into each other like a Teutonic tamale, *I Pagliacci* blares from the heavens, the steering wheel freewheels and the truck slides sideways and overturns, sending chickens and goats and mothers nursing babies and giant sacks of flour and everything else in the world and Germans and hepatitis in one fantastic kaleidoscope of human endeavor, catapulting out the back.

Finally twigging that they inhabit a universe that does not love them, Eckaru and company emerge from the mud and carnage alert and basically unhurt, probably because they'd grown to anticipate disaster. This is not the luck of everyone. And to think of the injustice that follows – blame and abuse descending upon the driver while the real culprit shoulders his pack and slinks away unmolested.

Eckaru had inquired of the driver how far was the next village and was told “about two miles.” After walking what he judges to be four or five of those with no sign of anything, Eckaru lays down his hepatitis in the mud and rain and has the best night's sleep he can remember.

Of course the fascinating part missing from the story is how the truck was got back up. That would have been worth seeing.

A new day dawned and with it a new brand of luck for the Teutonic travelers, having finally used up the other kind. At a village another few miles down the mud they were welcomed, brought into a hut, given dry clothes and made to sit around a fire with cups of hot tea in their hands and Eckaru judged he'd never been happier. That was easy to believe.

Happy and soon to be alone, as I found him, as we found each other. Well, who needs them anyway, Eckaru? Fair weather friends. Bah.

Why, you may ask, was Eckaru in Uganda? He had laid up in Kenya to recover from hepatitis and then started for Dar Es Salaam, the capital of Tanzania. This Kenyan border closure tends to throw people together. He was carrying a letter of recommendation to some political heavyweight there. It may have been President Nyere, I can't remember. His contact was through a relation. In Uganda he had walked some in the fabled Mountains of the Moon, which made me start wondering what that would be like.

Tom and Eckaru for Tanzania

It had to be, don't you think? The dream team, remake of *Abbott and Costello in Africa* though it must be odd for Eckaru, who had expected to be looking at his girlfriend whom inscrutable fate has replaced with me. Big difference for an hour to make and no escaping it; Eckaru's original course irretrievable, maybe someone else walking beside her now. We would see if partnership would divide or multiply our pitfalls. It didn't take long.

We thought we'd head for a mountain village called Kigoro near the Rwanda border. As we sally forth, the reader must be wondering whose luck will prevail: Tom's good luck or Eckaru's cruel luck? Or will it become a composite luck attacking them simultaneously? Tom's luck has not failed him but Eckaru's has, yet they are even, both still alive.

The essential difference being that Eckaru's luck has been called upon to rescue him only from humiliation and lost love and has come up short. Tom, short in the important area of common sense, as in without, depends on luck to preserve more than his social life. Perhaps if Eckaru challenges his luck in this more binding way it too will acquit itself well.

Before we left Kabale, the Reverend Solomon Bekunda of The Church of Uganda thickened the plot. But who knows what even worse fate he may have detoured us from. Bekunda invited us to use his name at the girls' school at Kigoro for a place to sleep. Wow, I must have thought. Things just keep working out. Related to that boon, other names for the clergyman eventually would come to mind.

Kigoro squats in the shadow of the dark, imposing mountain straddling the Uganda – Rwanda border, the last known refuge of the mountain gorilla, these people having been killed off throughout much of their range.

We caught a ride on literally a pick-up truck where a passenger introduced to us a new banana treat – banana steamed in the skin. You eat the whole damn thing. This rounded me out nicely. I'd absorbed bananas every which way but in the skin, which I thought was poisonous. I am living proof that, properly prepared, the skin is edible. Another ride carried us to the mountain region with its fantastic landscape. We even passed a bamboo forest, the sort pygmies inhabit. I strained to see one but they were too small.

At Kigoro we unluckily found the Church of Uganda School for Girls. It being closed for the summer, we were allowed to stay in the dorm, another bad break; for what a dorm it was! As outer space saturated a dark building in a naturally dark part of what already is considered The Dark Continent, we sat on our respective top bunks monitoring sounds increasing above the ceiling and wondering what it could represent.

Of course we found out. We always find out the things we'd be happier not knowing. It's the marvelous wonders in life that must forever go unexplained. Our night went like this: the sounds have developed into something stampeding around atop the ceiling. Never before have I used lightly and will not start now, the word stampeding. If it evokes for the reader a herd of wildebeests thundering across your roof, you're on the right track. The view from outside must have been astounding, walls seething with whatever it was streaming in from the nearby bush.

"Ho, ho," you say, "what's a herd of something running around to you? They're in the attic. It's not like you're camped in a herd of elephants." Quite right but there came a change in the weather.

We all have seen it raining cats and dogs. As night fell farther the sky opened with no umbrella to save a fella and it started raining not cats or bats or Minnesota Fats, not vermicelli or fancy hats, rhinoceros soup or dis or dats, no, by gum, it was raining (you guessed it) rats. To combat this our arsenal boasted my Tanzanian-made candle and Double Happiness matches. Desperately I struck dud after dud until I feared all were duds. Then, as if I were Lucifer, a match burst into flame which I quickly transferred. Gratefully we watched my bold tower of wax hold the horde at bay. It seemed the problem was overcome. And by any of the usual standards of normalcy, it should have been.

Let me mention here that never while backpacking have I felt justified the weight of an extra candle on my back. As soon as you pack an extra candle, you have opened the door to depravity and through it will march extra water, wafers and wallabies and never again will you have a manageable load. Until I joined Eckaru this policy had sufficed.

One would have imagined in a continent celebrated for being Dark with no electric lighting outside cities, that they would make damn good candles, maybe the best darn candles in the world. They should have candles down. On the contrary, if one based his judgment on the tools available in Uganda for making and maintaining portable fire, he would conclude that fire had been recently invented and it was still in the experimental stage.

It seemed the Tanzanians, bowing to greater experience in this matter of ignition, modeled their candles after the infamous Double Happiness matches from that ancient and learned civilization China, the only brand available since the match factory in Kampala burned down.

Scene II opens with Abbott and Costell.. er, me and Eckaru sitting on either end of a top bunk, all hope and concentration pitted on our first and only line of defense blazing between us.

As long as the candle melts, the herd is repelled and we need strike no further "matches." We are "Happy enough." So we have good reason to believe we are set. I never saw a candle that once afire didn't last to the bitter end; except this one. They had somehow built into it the hilarious joke of suddenly sputtering like a sparkler and going out.

"Those matches were well named. It's double happiness for the Chinese because only one out of three works," Eckaru deadpans as vermin bound across his lap and I throw down failed match after failed match. I think that makes it triple happiness but maybe the Chinese weren't being literal.

The varmints are playing musical chairs over us:* Round and round the ceiling they gallop and the instant that flame quits and darkness is complete again, the critters that happen to be over us

---

* strikingly similar to the Cairo cab drivers

right then get to descend and hop all over our beds and tear at our food bags in the pitch black.

Having had enough of this scene, the writer now makes it you and Eckaru and you're trying to relight the infuriating candle with the sarcastically named matches and maybe you're on a real streak and you hit six in a row that bring no joy. You're frantic. Do you feel it? You're starting to fear you'll empty the box before another one responds. And then what?!? The other rats, being dirty rats, are cheating and they're dropping in too and though, thank Joe DiMaggio you can't see anything, you hear them everywhere. Trying to deincentivize them, you suspend all food away from yourself and, Church of Uganda miraculously they never figure that out, also not figuring out you don't have it anymore, still jumping on you and ravenously hunting for it.

After repeated episodes with successively shorter periods of illumination the candle grows tired of the game of sputtering and then going out and simply refuses to be re-lit. Experience the frustration of that – you finally got a match to go and the candle pouts. (As I write this, it occurs to me that this may actually be a safety feature so people don't fall asleep and burn down the straw house.) Now it's me again. Thanks for jumping in there. We grabbed our stuff and got the Chinese matches out of there and pitched my tent outside, where we encountered giant flying insects; but we weren't all that impressed.

I'm pretty sure you could tie up the doctor from the Star Ship Enterprise in there and after a couple hours he'd fit his nickname. I intended to write a letter of thanks to Solomon Bekunda but I couldn't find the anthrax.

Since that was not a lethal situation, only Eckaru's luck answered, which, as we leave Uganda, I fear may become the pattern. We were looking forward to market day in this mountain village because of its interesting location near the borders of three countries. Some sellers told us they walked forty miles through the night with their goods for this. Most things had been smuggled into Uganda by going cross country at the border posts. People from the mountain brought excellent wooden bowls. They are as I was told: "The meal will be as hot at the end as it was at the beginning."

I bought all the wooden bowls I could for fifty cents each plus an astounding milk bottle carved from so-called monkey wood and got wrecked for it by Eckaru. He unfailingly chastised me for capitalistic outbursts, arguing the goods should stay here where people need them. At the time I couldn't see that but strangely, later I could. Maybe it's harder to see the point when self interest stands in the way. I bought the only two cardboard boxes in the village, wrapped them with vines and sent them from the local post office air mail to Orlando and that is exactly how they arrived at JFK airport and then my house plus some mildew. Air mail from Kigoro means on top of a bus for some time. I suppose they went through rain.

In Uganda the mysteries of economics were laid bare. I met an irate Uganda man at this market. He had traveled from my old haunt Kampala to buy all the Double Happiness matches at this remote spot on the frontiers of Rwanda, Uganda and Tanzania. In this way he was a capitalist pig like me. He intended to return to the capital and sell them. Along the way his bus had been stopped numerous times and he had been stripped of a large portion of the money he brought to purchase goods.

So – from excesses of the soldiers, fueled by skimpy pay if legitimate soldiers and no pay at all if bogus, we see why the residents of Kampala and vicinity are short on matches, which were anyway more of tinder than flame. Funnily enough they were highly esteemed by the locals. Apparently the Ugandan-made ones were even worse, but good enough to burn down the factory. This may provide incentive to build a fireproof match factory next time. Maybe make it out of Double Happiness matches.

On the other hand, thanks to the soldiers, his purchasing power is crippled so locals out here at the foot of the mountain will have dubious matches. The part less clear is the effect on China. I wonder if these were bad batches they wouldn't ship to countries that demand ignition or if these boxes of mostly useless matches to Africa was their whole game.

The irate businessman told of a fellow passenger who tried in vain to defend his luggage against the soldiers. He was a merchant carrying clothing and they took it, probably for any photo-ops down the line. I recall feeling heartened to see for a change a furious Ugandan and to hear of a defiant one.

However anyone *not* in uniform caught stealing at a market can expect to be beaten into eternity on the spot. Zero tolerance for civilian crime. I suppose that's trickle-down for you. Now we know where it trickled to. Definitely a strong deterrent as opposed to ***TIDE***.

This was hard to reconcile with the laid back way the people seemed. But Eckaru and I saw the sticks and boards flailing at something running through the crowd. We thought a cow must have invaded the market but it was a shoplifter trying to get away. In what I was told was a rare intervention, a policeman stopped the party before the presents were opened. Maybe it was his mother. I had become friendly with the two guys who ran the post office and asked them about it. They said they didn't like that sort of thing but I wasn't sure of their sincerity. Near us we saw it almost happen again as a dispute escalated nearly to that point between a seller and a woman.

One recreation always available to a Caucasian pedestrian in Uganda was the terrifying of small children merely by appearing before them. Yep. Nothing in their mothers' milk had prepared them for *that.* They would run screaming or crying into the nearest arms. I wonder how they would have reacted if I were two feet tall.

The scenery around there was lush, green rolling hills with a grass hut planted here and there, the odd extinct volcano thrown into the background for effect and planted fields that looked from above like patchwork quilts and shimmering lakes poured into the low spots. Not a bad set-up for idle strolling.

Being Eckaru, his ointment had attracted a big fat horsefly. He couldn't walk anywhere without a pack of kids in his wake. Dawn to dusk he looked like the Pied Piper of Hamlin and this really wore on the poor lad. I suppose this was the typical German in him finally peaking out. Everyone knows that once kids have gotten to a big person, and there's no hiding it from their instincts, they will persist until their object is a quivering puddle of ugali or their parents have called them home. In this way was Eckaru's pleasure in our surroundings degraded. For me it wasn't so bad as I enjoy celebrity and any crowd will do. If they did start to bug me, I usually could climb out of reach.

Celebrity good to a point. In practice, I literally couldn't take a dump without an audience. One evening, it had been a particularly spectacular sunset and, perhaps primed by this excitement, I was trying to find a place to unload in private but well-wishers stuck to me like flies to what they knew was coming and they wanted to be there when it did and see how a mzungu defecates; or perhaps they labored under tales from colonial times that white people have no need of it or their product is white or they enter mysterious rooms to deal with the problem, and they wanted to learn the truth.

Each time I found a likely nook, they crowded around. Surely Eckaru would have been the chosen one but I suppose, through some injustice of digestion, he didn't have to go. Maybe Germans really don't have to. And somehow they could tell I did. That entire citizenry was like a gator hunter aware that sooner or later his quarry must come up for air. They knew I hadn't done number two and I was due. It was too bad I lacked the foresight to sell tickets because their patience paid off. In the middle of the village nature no longer would be denied. I surrendered all modesty right there and gave everyone a clear view. I don't recall what happened to it.

But suppose I enjoyed showing off my facility with the bowels, finally tasting stardom, like I was *some*body. Unwilling to return to obscurity, I hand out fliers billing myself as

Bestin Intestine
Number One at Number Two
He poops to the King
Village Center

There I am next day holding it in, waiting for the crowd to gather. Tragically I can't even draw flies. They've seen it and checked it off their basket list – "See mzungu plant a deuce - done. Dung same color as Uncle Fred." Frantically I cast about for ways to improve the act, maybe add some dancing gorillas. And no, this isn't what happened. I said, "suppose."

Before leaving this base subject, I must credit Eckaru with introducing to me the raptures of the "full moon shit." He was right. It's sublime to squat out in the countryside contemplating the full moon while nature works her disgusting magic upon that delicious food you ate. If you haven't already, try it. You'll like it*.

The tempting lakes were some work to reach and then you couldn't swim from the bank due to the presence of Slopeye the Snailorman. Furthermore the natives said they held no fish except what they call a mudfish, a crazy looking catfish sort of thing with a pointed tail. So why go to them? My fishing ego was blown up so big at this point that I was sure my expertise and modern tackle would find fish they didn't know were there. And if they weren't there, perhaps my tackle would spontaneously generate them. So I

---

* The writer would like to call the reader's attention to the extent to which he has stretched his vocabulary to include this important section without crossing the boundary of tasteful language, using terms such as "dump", "defecate", "#2" etc. While he would be naturally inclined to leave out such details, he feels they are vital to a true account of his adventures and their anthropological value. For the sake of authenticity the direct quote from Mr. Wallis remained as spoken.

made my way down to the shore of Lake Mbotu where I caught nothing from the limited fishable space. A local with a dugout offered to drive me to the middle where it would be safe to swim. After a great swim I talked him into paddling me around the shore to cast the undefeatable squirrel tail jig into some very fishy looking spots. My failure to get a strike proved the natives correct.

Eckaru and I discussed visiting the mountain gorillas but the rains had come and we didn't feel like trying to slide up that old volcano. But suppose we did try and we got up there in terrible weather and a gorilla family invited us into their shelter and took care of us. Wouldn't that have been something?

Nilism

Beware of the boy

Charles

Out of Uganda

We bade adieu to the mountain village, the rat race and Uganda and embarked on the seven miles to the Rwanda border. The stupid canoe pack gave me no end of discomfort and regrets about leaving good, wonderful, faithful pack at home. In spite of this giant backward beer belly of a pox on life bouncing off my butt as I walked and which was forever trying to pull me backwards, it was a really nice walk that finished up with a eucalyptus forest. As I feared would happen, my visa had died so I had to skirt the crossing. It was pretty easy, one guy on the border post and vigilance wasn't his game. Of course Eckaru didn't even need a visa because he's a (Woohoo!) German.

I stepped out of Uganda and into the feeling of relief - like I could let out the deep breath taken on entering the country. This was a total surprise. Apparently people can be stressed with no way of knowing it until the cause is removed. I expected to lose the camera (which would come later) but at every roadblock I hid it successfully on the transportation. And, to paraphrase Pogo, it turned out I was the only real threat to my life.

And the coffee *was* incredibly cheap. As was postage. Nicely packaged pound bags of the stuff cost fifty cents each. It was eight bucks to buy and send a big box of them home, even in 1981 not much. And the phone calls *were* incredibly cheap; and clear as Ronald Reagan's conscience. I talked to the U.S. for ten minutes for a dollar and it sounded like my party was around the corner.

My time in Uganda seemed more like an anaconda than the

garter snake that it was. If you measure time by events, or the absence of the same thing happening twice, it *was* longer. Much longer, like I got to live a few months but lost only three weeks. I love that.

RWANDA

So far Eckaru and Tom – with the help of the rat Reverend Bakunda, we didn't take long to realize our potential. Maybe combined we won't have calamities any more than we would separately. Or we'll share each other's. It could be there's a finite number available in the environment and as a unit we'll suck them all up as we go.

From the frontier of Rwanda we began walking into this new country down the dirt road through a graceful eucalyptus forest. The change in the people was remarkable. Ugandans are warm and friendly. Rwandans are like chocolate Frenchmen. Bitter chocolate. Rwanda had been officially exploited by the French and part of their legacy, apparently, is a poopy attitude toward tourists.

As I walked down the road paranoid enough to be hoping a border guard would not come roaring up behind us to nab me for unauthorized entry, a vehicle approached, realizing my fears. Well, now what?!?

Never fear, Germany is here. Of course. As the white Mercedes Benz pulled alongside, Eckaru recognized the German ambassador to Uganda, just checking up on their last hope. He picked us up. Why can't my government provide me this kind of service? We won the war. Well, I guess one thing doesn't always lead to the other.

His original passenger was a German "educator" sent to Uganda some years earlier to, and get this, "establish the German language in Uganda." They don't know how to stop, do they? But an open minded person might ask why not? What could be more fun than a country of laid back Africans speaking the tongue of

The Farterland? Why shouldn't a Ugandan family sit in the hause in their liederhosen saying "Ach du liber! Pass the bratwurst you swine." "Danke shane." Later they could go out in the yard and yodel their brains out ... Twenty years pass and the infection has spread all across New Germany. And then...

I would have thought official Germans chagrined to see Africans mastering their language and then contaminating it to better use.

Regardless of what I would have thought, my illicit entry into Rwanda was being thoroughly laundered and I went from anxious to bulletproof. Looked like Eckaru could do good luck too.

Adolf got us to Ruengori, on the Rwanda side of the gorilla mountain and the base for all human observation. I suppose, having failed with the human population, Germany was restarting with these hairy fellows to then work they're way up. Or down, depending on your viewpoint. I wonder if the gorillas would know what language they were signing in.

Rwanda had the only chocolate since Nairobi but it was expensive by any standard. I abstained as the price would have tainted the flavor. Mysteriously everybody we met was dismissive or rude. Maybe, I concluded, the language itself fosters this.

We looked it up, down and sideways and resolved to try to visit gorillas, maybe the last chance before they started speaking German, which, I have to tell you, would absolutely wreck the experience. However that decision was soon made moot.

We came upon a hubbub outside the courthouse. From loudspeakers affixed to the building, the throng was monitoring inner proceedings. Though Eckaru took French in school, he couldn't parlez vous Rwandan. Sadly he lacked confidence even to try communicating with it. The next day we learned some revolutionaries were being tried for smiling at a tourist; zero tolerance here too. I was skeptical of their guilt, the charge being so far-fetched. Probably they had been smiling already about a tourist drowning or something when one walked in front of them.

One night in town and we found somebody to buy our money at slightly better than bank rate, hardly worth the risk but a principal was involved. The next day we were buttonholed by the police chief who declared our subliminal welcome expired because of the trial and would we please catch the next bus out of town. I was on pretty thin ice at that latitude to protest. He wouldn't have needed the trial as an excuse if he'd checked my visa. Probably thought I was a countryman of Eckaru and didn't need one. Bad timing to be found illegally in the country. Maybe my trial would have been next. I'll count that as a road gladly not taken.

I've been kicked out of a few things, never a whole town. I felt like a gunslinger. "Your kind ain't welcome around here," the marshal drawls. "Stage'll be leavin' in an hour. You'd best be on it."

The stage I was at was blowin' his goldanged head off and then takin' over the country. That's when Eckaru picked the wrong time to trot out his schooling, trying to explain we planned to visit our relatives the gorillas. Then the chief looked at us more deeply and, having been exposed to my French connection's abominable lingo, he thought better of his plan. Exhausting his year's supply of Rwandan hospitality, he insisted on personally driving us to the edge of town. That would've riled me some more but dang it, I can't resist a free ride. Under better circumstances we might have made it up there to meet Dian Fossey. Might have wound up volunteering with her. Having recently read more about Fossey up to her murder four years later, I would love to have met her and her hairy friends. There's a regrettable road not taken. Maybe her local opposition was the real root of our dismissal. Again, So near, yet so far. That's not an adage, it's a calamity. Never got fonda Rwanda. Bye bye mountain gorillas. Bye bye.

WARNING

Having gotten you to read this far, whoever you are, as your guide

I feel I have earned the right to editorialize. Skip it at your peril:

It's time for a reminder that all the foregoing trip around Lake Victoria to get to this next country would have been "the road not taken" had the border from Kenya been open. I simply would have entered Tanzania to see the Serengeti, my only reason for going and as it turned out, the least of it. Of course I still could have gone through Uganda; but totally blind to the possibilities, I wouldn't have. I was forced into something I lacked the wisdom to do voluntarily, unable to foresee that the adventure lay by the unbeaten path, and I think that's the key, that by sheer luck I escaped the confines of my preconceived notions. What a catastrophe *that* would have been had I not. All those people and places that populate my memory – and yours now - gone, never to materialize – how much less rich my life would be with no Kabalega Falls, no Johnny Kabagambe with my hot sponge bath - My God – no Eckaru! Even worse for him – no me!

But I would be ignorant of my poverty, just a lot of unrealized potential among all the rest. I could have turned around and done it all again no more than a spent hurricane can head back south to start over. Suppose I'd left Orlando a few weeks later than I did: I never meet Terry who's already in South Africa or killed somewhere by the dew, so now I'm about to enter Uganda alone. Or maybe with you. Who knows? Everything's basically the same but a little changed. Maybe this time the buffalo runs at me. Or it's a lion. Makes you wonder, doesn't it, about the undiscovered land in our lives - the roads not even imagined, the real Lost World.

How about all those years of repetition, eye on the paycheck, the pension and the pine box; the pine box – a destiny planted early and our whole time dragging us toward it like a winch. Trying to miss the target, we can't help aiming at it; every year a stepping stone through the future with *more* adventures squandered and fewer remaining, just hoping to get out of body with a modicum of dignity; maybe makes sense on the moon where there's not much to do but here? To dismiss such bounty with noses to grindstones, eyes on the road and ears to the ground may be the gravest sin of living in this age of opportunity– of all the animals we might have been, forfeiting the liberty that comes with being modern man.

Suppose we were constantly aware of all the experiences we could have had, better than whatever we did have, inside a kaleidoscope of constantly rotating snippets of what might have been. Maybe that's why we have the useful truism “Ignorance is bliss.”

TANZANIA – the hard way

I would like to point out that I'm about to reach Tanzania. If you've been paying attention, you know absolutely no skill or intelligence was expended in this feat so I should have plenty left for the remainder of the book. That in itself, though, was pretty smart, eh? Learning to think ahead.

This shows anybody can do it. You head for a place and apparently you get there. Must be the way the planet's set up. That would be pretty boring except for the journey.

Rwanda roads were the best paved of the trip, closely resembling U.S.A. roads and our trip to the border was uneventful. We filled up with turbid water from the red river at the border post and embarked on a fourteen mile walk to the first Tanzanian town. Our new landscape, hot and parched, was a stark contrast to the rich, fertile Uganda. We saw small huts of straw sitting atop spindly legs about thirty feet high. They remain a mystery. My pack was trying to kill me. The path was up and down all the way. It actually was a dirt road but in two days we saw no vehicle.

Eckaru's once reasonable backpack hung to one side having blown a connection so we were becoming a matched set. He had the water a hill ahead of me. Hot and thirsty I rested under probably an equally parched tree. Folks came to see if I was alright (this works every time). They led me to their straw house and offered one of the best drinks of my life – banana water, whatever that is. (Who knows? Maybe it's their euphemism for urine). I never got it again. And it was cool. They had a kind of natural refrigerator in a small alcove in a wall.

That was interesting. Unlike the U.S. where everybody has whatever is in stores, people here had individualized treatments of bananas that I would see only once.

My pack having failed yet again to finish me off, I caught up with my buddy. We camped that night by an acacia tree at the edge of a cliff overlooking a starkly different world – a vast expanse of flat jungle far below with a river winding through it. How that river called to me and how inaccessible it was. I still want to fish in it.

Taken as a whole it was a grand hike. Scattered along the way entrepreneurs sat by the left side of the road with wonderful banana treats for sale (always up for more variations). Usually it was a few women per group each with her own little pile of goodies. From what we'd seen of the road, business must have been slow. Real slow. Good thing we came along.

Lacking guidelines for this sort of thing, I followed the sensible Eckaru's stated policy which was "Always buy from the ugliest woman. This is the one who has striven hardest for quality and a bargain price." We learned that even the ugliest woman is more beautiful when she smiles.

As we sat by the road enjoying local bounty, a boy rode up on a bicycle made of wood. Perhaps an earlier Raleigh, I thought. It lacked only pedals so the boy pushed along with his feet as he sat on it. In my frequent stupor about some things, I thought only "Ah! Here comes a boy riding a wooden bicycle." After observing Eckaru's astonishment like he'd seen something remarkable and hearing him rhapsodize about it matching a picture in a schoolbook showing "the first bicycle" I began to appreciate what a small thing this made of the Raleigh. We all need a nudge in the right direction from time to time.

With my camera out the kid, a natural star, kept posing for me so I waited for a candid shot which never came, poser that he was. I figured we must have discovered the land of wooden bicycles and I'd see more which I never did, probably why the kid was so up himself; so I didn't get a picture of a wooden bicycle. I regret that. I wonder if the bike was made for this boy or if it had been handed down.

The ingenuity of the locals expanded my idea of possible. I had heard about marvelous Sudanese toys and here was the Tanzanian version. Along this road we saw a boy playing with a car on a flexible pole about four feet long. A cat could fit in the car. It was made entirely of wood with a positraction suspension and the rod was the perfect propellant. I tried it and it worked splendidly. You could see the suspension keeping the ride smooth. Made me ponder how much care went into making that toy compared to going to K-Mart and picking something up. I realized most Americans cheat themselves of this satisfaction and joy, instead investing their time in a job and then watching television. Imagine how exciting to make an amazing gift and present it and how appreciated it would be. You can have fun with an assembly line gift but I suspect the joy factor must be installed with love.

{If you're wondering if I learned from this observation, thereby giving hope to modern man, the answer is "Maybe." Against all odds I wound up with progeny and I made them a playhouse, a sandbox and a tree platform. These were indeed imbued with joy and received with the same. But I never was a handy guy in the first place.}

At this point a dietary flaw was revealed by persistent little cuts in my mouth. Mom had identified that long ago as a vitamin c deficiency. I hadn't seen citrus since leaving Kenya but we came to a hot, dusty marketplace with lemons. I forced myself to eat some though a smart man or an optimist would have made lemonade. Still saving my brains for later, I guess. Too late I remembered the excellent old saw, "When life gives you lemons don't eat them." At least it worked and scurvy was averted.

Here's another one, regularly illustrated. "A rich man saves his snot while a poor man throws his away." This of course is a tribute to the handkerchief and favorite proof of the smug superiority of poverty.

"Looky here, you rich dandy, why you foldin' up yer snot and puttin' 'er in yer pocket? Afride you'll run out? Watch me. See, I just blows it on the ground. I don't need it. And on yer shoe. Well, just wipe it up. There's some extry for ye."

They were experiencing a Kleenex shortage in the fourth world just then so I would have blown my nose with firewood but they were short of that too. Luckily I had brought a couple Kleenexes, never skilled with the farmer blow, a holdover, I suppose, from when I was rich. As an example for all civilization, I reveal here that I leaned my used tissues against grass blades to dry and be recycled. It required a small investment of time but worked surprisingly well. There we have it - planet saved. I didn't have much else to do anyway.

Our trek ended at The Town that Had a Bus but Didn't (have a bus). So named because our inquiries after a bus elicited, "Yes." It would arrive at such and such a time at that end of town. That time and place came and went without the hoped for ingredient and then we asked someone else and got another time and place that came and went while we remained, like we had walked into a dimension where people just make shit up.

You might not see much reason to agree, but me and Eckaru, we're smart. After a couple days playing "Phantom Bus," somebody told us there was no bus. We instantly recognized the first opinion matching the evidence. I like to think we would have concluded that on our own eventually but as they say, a word to the wise is like a paragraph to a Republican. The people were trying to help us in our terms. For them it arrives when it gets there. Or Hell freezes over. Probably at some point in their lives each had seen a bus at the place and time they recommended. We found two guys driving a truck to Mwanza, a town on the south shore of Lake Victoria.

My last vantage point on that lake had been Hippo Point in Kisumu, Kenya where I pointed at a Hippo about a lifetime ago. The truckers weren't overly friendly and we were all that day and the morning of the next battling over price. We agreed at shillingi mia mbili hamsini. (You can see the writer has become so easy with Swahili that now he writes it without thinking.)

Tanzania was sporting a strangely inflated value of its currency, bank rate eight per dollar, putting it over the shining star of East Africa, Kenya, at ten. I never understood that but the black market seems a truer gauge of the currency's value. Black market was forty to the dollar which was great. For me. I had an eighty percent discount off what locals paid. Could be simply a way to keep poor people poor. Those with dollars pay one thing, those without keep scraping by at five times the rate. Black market for the well heeled, banks for the rabble. Because of this the trucker would receive the equivalent of thirty bucks (bank rate) while costing us only three each. Kind of a win-win. It was a little better than Uganda's three to one but for our purposes it was back in the right ballpark. Puzzling also that you get 250 shillings per dollar in Uganda and forty in Tanzania and the result is about the same, like it's the ratio of the rates that matters and not the dollars. Don't get it, just appreciated it.

We heard of a German jailed in Dar es Salaam after changing with a kid on the street, a big no-no. It sounded like he'd been entrapped. A kid did approach me on the street pestering me for an American dollar. Back to our ride -

It would be a full day to Mwanza. We rode a tarp stretched over the back of the truck; a big truck, coulda held chickens, goats nursing women, sacks of flour and all the honest congressmen. Well, they coulda rode in the ash tray. But in defiance of unnatural law, it held only us. With an empty bed we were riding a bucking trampoline all day as we bounced, flounced and everythingounced along the dirt road, throwing up cumulus clouds of red dust and elephant dreams. Tree limbs harried us at noggin level so instead of ducking ahead of time as did the more conservative acrobat, the Amazing Eckaru, I made a game of waiting until the last instant. This left no room for the unexpected. Always a mistake not to expect that. Inevitably the truck lurched up at the moment I ducked so I got a taste of what I deserved, just a graze. I quit while I had a head.

The guy who wasn't the driver (thank goodness it was him and not the other one) would climb out his window from time to time and ride the bronc with us. Either the driver was flatulent or it looked like that much fun. No two ways about it, it was a jolly ride. The standard technique for staying on was to hold the tarp with at least one hand and sometimes three or four at all times. This served the dual purpose of limiting launch height and ensuring you landed back on the tarp when you came down or it came up to meet you. Still it wasn't foolproof and in a moment of lapsed vigilance I nearly ate clay. I guess that would have looked funny if I didn't break anything.

After touring all kinds of scenery we sure enough wound up in our first major Tanzanian town, Mwanza. We hopped down and I presented the driver with his fare which he steadfastly refused, casually dismissing my attempts to pay. Then I offered it to the other guy. No dice, he wouldn't touch it either. No big deal, they just weren't interested in taking the money we negotiated over tooth and nail for two days.

I would meet more Africans who love to debate and I suspect this driver was one. Either our relationship changed over the course of the day or they never intended to reach beyond the virtual shillings we fought with. Likely the source of puzzlement was my origin where money pervades our days like blood through our bodies and must be vigilantly maintained; because if we stop grabbing it, we'll be sucked under by the quicksand of society.

The reader might be noting this is not the first time Africans refused my cash. Perhaps money occupies a rung or two lower in the hierarchy of considerations in some places, the side show, not the main event. In any case, any place, ability to eschew it undeniably is a strength. "Nope, sorry. Don't want your money. You keep it. You may need it." Whoda thunk it?

We stayed around town a couple days, shopkeepers unreceptive to swapping currencies, probably related, we felt, to that German getting busted. Finally Eckaru found a man planning to travel and needing better currency. One compensation for Eckaru not needing visas was the uselessness of his Deutch Marks on the black market. Either dollars or Kenya shillings were required, the bigger the denomination and more immaculate the condition, the better. But no Deutch Marks.

The Mwanza produce market was odd in that prices were marked on the goods. I suspected this a set-up for tourists to pay more though it hardly would have been worth it as we seemed to be the only tourists. A skinflint anyway, I tried bargaining with a woman over her banana prices to avert being duped. She didn't bargain back. She thought I must be broke so she handed me a bunch for free. I felt pretty microscopic then and coughed up her price. Was that her saying, “It works every time?”

I intended to hitchhike through the Serengeti, even for me an impractical idea and Eckaru had his sights on a bus to Dar es Salaam so I saw him off and good-bye Eckaru. So ends the experiment. I judge it a success. Eckaru's birthday was coming and I sent him a card. Don't know if he got it. The boy never seemed robust and I wondered if he made it alright.

I stayed in Mwanza a couple days more because a nice hot meal of beef and rice was so cheap that I had two suppers every night, one for each stomach. I had heard food would be scarce in Tanzania, Fourth World and all but I ate there like a capitalist pig. I bought an amazing carved wooden tea service that I esteem highly and nobody else does, some bowls and some baskets “woven so tightly that they hold water.” I sent it all to Orlando dirt cheap and it arrived with the tea tray broken and some bags of candy to make up for it.

Do they Speak Spaghetti in the Serengeti?

Here's a riddle: How do you start hitchhiking to the Serengeti?

With your thumb out!!! My first taker was Laane Skaans, a Danish school marm of all things. She and her husband were working there on a contract with the Danish government. She suggested I take a day or two off from my quest and accompany her to see some snake dancers she knows. (I know. It never stops, does it? This place is like a roulette wheel in The World Casino where all numbers pay off.)

That's right, I figured thyme and tide may wait for no man but Serengeti Betty would wait for me. Never heard of snake dancers, not serpent what that would be, maybe dancers that look like snakes. Here we go into new horizons. Laane found them practicing in a field, drummers and all, good timing on my part. They were preparing for a snake dancer's competition – public not invited. It's betwixt themselves, needing no cheering crowds to egg them on.

Turns out it's men dancing with snakes. They lacked partners but went through the motions as if they didn't. In case you're wondering, it's not garter snakes. They were waiting on somebody supposed to come out the jungle with a python. This is the sort of place it is. You need a python? "Hey Pete – you're not doing anything - go get us a python. Monty forgot his."

"Oh alright," he says, slowly rising off his haunches. "What size?"

"Well," says the dancer in his lovely accent, "too small to eat you but big enough to try."

Pete chuckles ruefully.

The Skaans' daughter had grown up there, so far to about five. It was captivating to see her little blonde pony tail out there bouncing along dancing with the local kids. She wanted more than anything else though, as all little Danish girls should, to have her own snake to dance with. She could speak Danish, Swahili and the local language. Or – she was in Denmark playing with Legos and watching Sesame Strasse. I wonder if they would have become the same adult and I wonder what she's doing now.

One drunk guy in an overcoat twirling alone was singing an obnoxious song about mzungus, no doubt in our honor, one of the few times I heard that as a slur.

I pitched my tent outside Laane's hut and met her husband Andy Capp in the morning. After a few days binge in Dar, as it's called by thems in the know, he arrived home still drunk and unshaven, regarded me with a suspicious eye and handed his wife a little toy sailboat to smooth the seas but the gift was a little smashed, too.

Laane brought me back out the road and introduced me to Hitchhiker Heaven, which naturally has a catch. After extensive thumbing, I feel qualified to amend that depressing reminder oft visited by the experienced upon the innocent, that "Nothing in life, not even hitchhiking, is free."

I'm sorry to report this seemingly carefree mode of transport is ruled by cruel, unfailing corollaries of Smurfy's Law. (Feeling overworked and underpaid, Murphy delegated to his even meaner understudy the contamination of the best things in life, which were supposed to be free.) This included hitchhiking: "The likelihood of getting a ride is directly proportional to the desirability of one's environment and the prospects it offers." Of course inseparable from that is "The more intolerable your situation, the greater time will elapse between rides." So- good is always mitigated, bad exacerbated. Does that sound familiar?

The track I thumbed bisected a pleasant little village anchored in the middle by a big, friendly shade tree and this is where Laane deposited me. Looking back, I believe this was Smurfy setting me up for regret. He knows tree shade is my favorite kind, rotating through the day, affording the occupant varying vistas and the choice between dappled shade and the solid bar cast by the trunk in *The Grapes of Wrath*.

I stationed myself under this shield against the equatorial sun and received women and children selling local treats. I had money enough to buy every treat they could manufacture for the next three years and I was well prepared to do it. In Uganda I'd had my fill of adventures. Comfort and security were mine now and I didn't give an elephant shit popsicle if I ever got picked up. In short, this would do.

In later years when visitors inquire about the mzungu under the tree, villagers will reply, "Oh, he's hitchhiking to the Serengeti Plain."

The visitors will say, "Oh."

On hearing this mild exclamation, I will turn and grant a beatific smile. I would become the legendary "man under the tree." People will draw graffiti on me, write limericks about me, like

There was a man under the tree
thumbing to the Serengeti.
His progress was slow
For he had lots of dough
And for leaving he was never quite reti.

Yes, there it is, the reader is quite correct. It was all an excuse for me to write a poem. You never know, though. Robert Frost might have got his start this way.

As we know, I had less chance of retaining this idyllic spot than an anopheles mosquito has of translating the Declaration of Independence into Esperanto. On a dark and stormy night. Smurfy his own miserable blue self probably leading the charge, the foregoing legislation was enacted against me. I believe in my heart that no real people were around to carry out the enforcement so the unlikely characters who appeared on the road out of a cloud of dust were created on the spot; and with precious little attention paid to making them believable. Even the pretense of coincidence got nary a nod.

There I was leaning against my, that's right, my tree just

digging into some native delicacy which presaged many to come when three open Land Rovers that five minutes before had not existed, ground to a halt in front of me. Each carried a cliche' just sprung to life who could thank me for it and never bothered to. Oddly they seemed more astonished at seeing me out there thumbing than they were at their own instant existence which the brave fellows took in stride, another exciting tribute to human adaptability. Being flung straight from oblivion into a Land Rover crossing Tanzania isn't something I'd take lightly but then, I'm not English.

Here's what Smurfy came up with for me: three extremely white Englishmen: a rugged looking one got up as an adventurer, cork-hat and all, we'll call him Ramar; an older, short one with one of those around-the-mouth "Look at me I've been sucking on a sewer pipe" mustaches who looks like and is a cantankerous stick-in- the -mud; one who needs only a tray in his delicate hands to look like he can't find anyplace to sit in the secondary school cafeteria and a pitch black Negro named Magazini. The three Englishmen are made to be entomologists. Akin to that obscure superhero the Flying Dutchman who zooms around Holland plugging dikes, they're chasing across Tanzania a maize crop-destroying beetle destined to lay waste to the entire Dark Continent if'n they can't figure out something. The black Negro is a jovial sort and he's made to be the convoy's African guide.

As long as he's doing it, I don't see why Smurfy stops there. Why not have me picked up by Stanley, Livingstone and Lawrence of Arabia? Furlough Nelson Mandela for the guide?

Each Englishman has his own vehicle so they don't have to talk to each other, the only realistic part, and the guide has his choice of the three. He chooses Ramar. To lend credibility to the African's name, they tell me a story about another African born while a German mechanic was fixing a carburetor in his village. It ain't exactly coming in with Haley's Comet but there it is. Able then to imagine the circumstances of Magazini's birth, I no longer considered his name remarkable.

After all I was ostensibly trying to find the Serengeti and they were going my way regardless of their origin. I gave the tree a good-bye pat on the bark and got in with the young one named Rick Hodges. He revealed that they were taking a break from saving Africa and heading for the Serengeti. Whoa! Aside from my hay wagon full of girls belatedly showing up, this was beginning to sound like the best possible scenario. But I would have to play my cards right, I'd done this before and I knew the drill. As a hitchhiker sometimes you want to ingratiate yourself to the driver to stretch out the ride. Like on the airplane where you always hope to land a lift from your seatmate; all these small potatoes to what was at stake here. What a great way this would be to visit the Serengeti and it was down to me to let it happen.

I suspected Rick, being a young guy, would like some company rolling through the immense plain. I can talk science and I showed him I could but I didn't want to overdo it, just enough to presage some interesting conversation. At the last place he could let me off before the vast plain of death, I pleaded my case for accompanying them all the way. He petitioned the others and the white people voted. That seemed somehow familiar to me, couldn't quite place it. It was 2 - 1 in favor. Yahoo! You know who cast the nay vote.

To New York with my tree. I know what you're thinking and I don't mind saying it: Thanks, Smurfy. If you ever need a job, I'd recommend you for tour operator.

Back when innocent of Africa and all that was to come there, I felt that most of all, I wanted to see the famed Serengeti. And now, this is how it would happen. But that person who imagined it, he never made it there. He never stood a chance. I didn't mind, I think the new guy could appreciate it more.

The road through Serengeti is a dirt track and we saw lions, giraffes, a servile cat and hyenas. The first lion Rick and I saw had been overlooked by the others. We spotted him and pulled off the track and drove to within ten yards of the big bruiser. He was a young adult just lion there under a small tree with a passion fruit smoothie. The wife was not far, lion in a similar position behind a log, covered in cubs as she tried to catch up on Serengeti Woman's Day. With bignoculars Rick could make out she was reading *The Truth about Tsetse Flies – Do We Really Need Them?*

I tried to talk Rick into driving closer perchance to take extremely cute photos but he feared that with another interruption of her reading, she might join us in our vehicle.

Well, it was all a revelation for me. This ain't no anthropomorphism. Lions really are just like Americans.

In all my wild animal whizdumb I felt the only real danger were the tsetse flies. They hate humans, so to us and any domestic animals that penetrate their domain they impart the usually fatal sleeping sickness. From the native fauna, with whom they have struck a deal, they withhold this gift, reserving the entire plain for wild animals whose sole obligation is to attract rangers and tourists. Yes, they are the original environmentalists.

With murder in their tsetse-bitsy hearts, they were invading the cars where our only job was to get them first, like Tiny Tim would. In the movie *Fail Safe* the U.S. military mixes in unarmed decoy planes with armed planes to distract the defenders, allowing planes with A-bombs to sneak through to Moscow. The Serengeti features a decoy fly that won't kill you but emits a burning juice if squashed on the skin. If you can't tell the difference between it and a tsetse fly, and there isn't much, this will discourage you from smashing flies on your body thus helping the killers detonate their bombs. So it was good to be able to distinguish them and devote undivided attention to the real danger. Always, it seems, it's lucky to be with entomologists. Thanks again, Smurfy. Maybe not such a bad guy after all, old Smurf; just misunderstood like a lot of us.

What we dreaded was any kind of a breakdown, with three vehicles triple the odds of it happening. So one of the Rovers broke an axle. Thanks again.

Now I shall ask Rod Serling, who has been smoking cigarets out behind the building, to step into the Serengeti and continue the narrative. Mr. Serling:

"Five men and one marvel of modern technology rendered as useful as a cave man's club on the moon, stranded in a vast plain on planet Earth that no human being has ever called home." Rod lifts his Chesterfield and takes a satisfying drag. "Never called home because (slapping his face) "home" implies something to miss while you're away, and there is nothing here (throwing down his cigaret to slap at both sides of his neck) for any man but misery, struggle and death. As our travelers know all too well, (clapping hands in front of his face) the air is home to tiny, identical bits and pieces of a nightmare." A lioness strolls by behind him looking back over her shoulder. "If these fragments draw together and find them, it will be (flailing his arms and talking faster) a nightmare these men can wake up from only in... *The Tsetse Zone*. Now get me outta here."

This is the point in *The Hound of the Baskervilles* where the guy goes from securely riding in the cozy coach through the spooky, howling night to falling out and being left behind. The horror had begun.

Luckily we had a spare axle. The time removing the old axle and installing the new one was far more perilous as we were sitting shmucks, easily swarmed upon. It was just a matter of how long before they homed in on us. Like zombies, one bite and you're done for. Add to this we were getting broiled by the unabated Sun of a Serengeti.

To keep them away, we all sang the tsetse fly song:

Tsetse fly, tsetse fly
Gonna slap you tsetse fly
Rather be a hand than a
stupid tsetse fly.

Why oh why did God create
That damned old tsetse fly.

No man live here
That's for sure
Sleepin' sickness
Got no cure

Why oh why did God create
That damned old tsetse fly.

In keeping with the authenticity of this story, I admit I just made up that song. Vigilance precluded singing. But not bad, eh? Looking at it, I'm thinking it would do. If this book writing gig doesn't pan out, I may have another avenue. The reader should feel free to add a verse or two and take it with him when he goes.

I have to say Land Rovers are for soccer moms. I've seen one stuck in the mud and now this. Apparently they're so prone to broken axles that people know to carry an extra one. We had lots worse terrain with good ol' Suzuki and nary a hitch.

We guarded each others' skin, especially the men doing the work, mainly Magazini and Ramar, necks and hands the favored landing zones. It was a race against the clock. Much of the time we appeared to be in a Three Stooges-esque brawl.

Look - what's that fuzzy, low, dark cloud in the distance moving our way? A sand storm or a monstrous swarm of flies to engulf us and make redundant all our slapping while droning to us the hideous lullabye of the Serengeti? Yep, we felt delivered with the axle in place and we could pile back in and blast the Hell off with no one infected. Looking back, probably just as well Eckaru wasn't along. Thinking of the lad, this incident shows everything's not my fault. Hallelujah. It wasn't even my Land Rover that broke.

A remarkable looking lodge has been built into boulders improbably poking up out of the savanna. My hosts were booked in and they had an extra bed so, so was I. Thank you Queen. You're the man. By far it was my best accommodation in Africa, maybe my whole life. No mystery toilet, shower and everything. Yep. Things were going my way, further confirmation that it's best to put one's fate in the hands of Smurfy where all good possibilities are waiting.

Now the sunset has done with me and I join my pals in the lap of luxury to monitor the Serengeti through a picture window. It reminds me of *The Veldt* by Ray Bradbury. It took awhile but at last I'm doing something in Africa like I might have imagined doing. I have been treated to a highly delicious liqueur called Africcocoa made in Tanzania and oddly enough shipped to England where it is bottled and cannot be bought, then returned to Tanzania where it can be bought but not bottled.

Next stop – Ingorongoro Crater, where Magazini acquits himself poorly. To enter the crater we were required to bring a guide – African looking guy to the fore. Guide was beyond his level of competence. He was bad at it and to underscore his apathy toward this place, he left his trash where we picnicked, by the elephant skull.

Being the crater of an extinct volcano and partly underwater, everybody comes there for a drink, like cruising Steak 'n' Shake. We drove to the floor and saw lions, flamingos, wildebeests, zebras, gazelles, giraffes, hyenas, kangaroos, etc. Also we saw the animal I most wanted to see; a rhinoceros and it was a mother and her cute little baby. Yep. Even rhinos start out cute.

The amazing gracefulness of giraffes running was something new for me. It is dumbfounding to witness the fluid motion that overcomes their inertia and starts them moving. Giraffefulness would be the better word but I doubt there's anything else it could be applied to.

Ramar had a huge cannon-like telephoto lens with which he

was always photographing stuff we couldn't even see. Or pretending to. He always wanted to see a leopard and had been here before, hoping to get lucky. Disappointment would strike again. We all were willing to stay around and go back down the crater to give him another shot, except Old Sewer Sucker, so we left. Must be another Murphy corollary - "Stick-in-the-muds rule." As life is unjust, no doubt also from the ubiquitous Irishman, soon I would accidentally realize Ramar's holy grail.

From Ingorongoro Crater to Odulvai Gorge, I have to say "Where do they come up with these great names?!?"

We only peered into the gorge from the edge. It was a big moment for my buddies as the site of some of the oldest known human bones. Which made me realize how self centered are humans. Of all the species still alive, only our own oldest bones are significant, only our evolution do we find compelling. You'd think the rest of it was context for us, the main event. What if our isolated outlook and dictionaried code is the result of being the only animal incapable of inter-species communication? Out of the loop again. There also was a gorgeous yellow bird in the middle of a thorn bush.

We drove out of there, crossed some land on a bitumen road and arrived without macaroons or macaroni in Makayuni where we parted ways. I noticed I had lost some of my independence with these guys, quite happy to let them do for me whatever they would. Though very tired, Rick drove me to a lodging that I paid for myself and then he drove off into the oblivion whence he had come. I was on my own again. From people selling them on the street I bought batiks, and whimsical oils on Masonite by Ntegu. Averse to risk sending these by Tanzanian air mail, I added to my burden by carrying everything with me.

My next trick would be crossing the one way border that repelled me into my odyssey. The turnstile worked toward Kenya but only with police permission, to be applied for in Arusha. In Nairobi I had obtained certain papers to smooth the crossing process.

I had asked Mom to send me my good backpack, and the bracelets from Baleisa should have arrived. Away from Nairobi far longer than expected, I feared the post office would send the things back. So, says I, to heck with Arusha. I'll head straight for the border and something will work out.

In sight of the crossing I approached stealthily, observing locals passing freely through the gate. Surveillance accomplished, I figured I'd blend in and cross unnoticed, the same solid reasoning as a burning light bulb hiding in the dark. That darn Smurfy again? "The more different you look from everyone else, the more likely you'll be spotted by a border guard and stopped?" No, probably not, gonna except full responsibility for this one. I pushed my luck. Right out the door.

That was disappointing. This fruitless excursion had put me two days more behind schedule for having to head back to Arusha which had been much closer before. Arusha ho!

Dissolving in a wooden chair at the Arusha police station was a Japanese guy who said he'd been waiting two weeks for the permission. This was bad news. However I had heard that Africans commonly dislike Japanese and I hoped the cause was good old prejudice, not red tape. I'm not sure if it was but I got permission that day while his contract was renewed. Reminds me of another embargo. I wonder if he ever got across.

I didn't bother to walk up that improbable bump Mt. Kilimanjaro because that was officially prohibited without hiring a local to carry one's pack. If, unlike the straw man, I had a brain, I would have recognized a good thing, a wonderful opportunity. Instead suddenly I felt proprietary about lugging my monstrosity around, wasn't going to skip on ahead with some poor local schlepping the white man's burden. Came here to see Mt. Kilimanjaro, not see from it. It might have been the grandest thing of all. At almost four miles up, I probably could have waved at Mom. I don't know – three words that cover a lot of ground.

I returned with a ticket to the scene of my earlier defeat and blithely walked from one country into the buffer zone of the next. It had been an eventful trip to Tanzania. Overall I must say the Serengeti is like a bagel. You may take it with cream cheese but I prefer my Serengeti plain.

mystery house

Eckaru lookin' for luck in all the wrong places

snake dancin'

What truth in advertising looks like

Every beetle's nightmare

Just lion around Ingorongoro Crater

Campsite with a view

KENYA II

The patient reader mustn't fear that with the writer back in good old Kenya, the story will continue as boring as these last few pages have been. It seems there's always something.

I walked into the little border village of Namanga, a funny place that looked like a South o' the Border stand. With no luck getting a ride out of there, it began to look like I'd be spending the night. But I didn't want to stay in Namanga. I was like a starving dog chained to the Eiffel Tower with a meal just out of reach. August eighteenth I had stepped out of Kenya and it was now September twenty-ninth. During that time I ate only bland food and no sweets. If you want to smuggle something in there, smuggle chocolate. In Rwanda a small chocolate bar went for ten dollars. Now in the home stretch, all barriers down, my taste buds were straining for some of that good Nairobi cookin'.

My fists clenched, tears welled in my eyes and I dropped to my knees. After all I'd been through, it was here, so near my goal, that I had a nervous breakdown. I pounded the earth with my fists and with eyes uplifted cried out, "Please, Smurfy, let me stay always in Namanga. I love it here so much. It reminds me of the Florida Turnpike." Then I started flying around backwards like a balloon until I plopped limply back to Earth.

This worked and a mutatu pulled up, the driver having seen me flying around. I dusted myself off like it was just nothing and got in. Of course it was an interesting ride. Each time we stopped, the countryside exploded with passengers either standing by the road peeing and snotting, or hunting up a bush for a more disgusting effort. People not so engaged would be squatting on their haunches as if they'd been there all day.

Opposite the way people normally hail a cab, this driver hailed his fares. Whenever he spotted a Masai walking beside the road, the enterprising fellow would pull alongside to coerce him into joining us. Masai are pretty easy-going so usually they agreed. First we appropriated a couple Masai women. They were quite brave to get in and they did it with an air of daring, like Terry and I heading into Uganda.

They were doing alright until the blowout. Yes, just like American women, Masai women scream at peril. Their worst fears realized, these two could not have looked more terrified with a crocodile on them. To say they were ecstatic when the Agent of Chaos quit shaking and they could plunge back into the normal world and stop screaming would be understating things. And I never would do that. We lost them as did, I imagine, all future mutatus.

Next he talked some goatskin clad young Masai men into going for a ride. While we still were stopped, one of these fellows leaned out the mutatu where there was no door and, a finger against one nostril proceeded to make a dilettante of my lady caller at the Iqbal who filled the sink from her nose. He purged a flow of green lava from the open nostril that he might have balanced on while releasing it. Where that astounding quantity of matter or anti-matter came from exceeded my grasp of nature. It is no stretch to say I had witnessed a paranormal event, as if he were siphoning it through the tires and up his body from some repository below the planet's surface (Probably Mauna Loa subsided slightly during this drain). I feared the vehicle would become mired in the extraction and unable to proceed.

It is my impression that Africans spend most of their time between rides ejecting something from their bodies: either pissing, number twoing, coughing up sputum or blowing snot all over the scenery. But I knew I wasn't simply an easily impressed tourist because this Masai's display actually grossed out the driver, who looked at me sympathetically and shook his head, even continuing to do so after he had resumed driving.

Let me say here that obviously it is no small thing to disgust with bodily discharge an African cab driver; and when I saw what it actually takes to do it, I abandoned any aspirations of my own. I know when I'm out of my league with my poor belches and farts. If bodily discharge ever becomes an Olympic event (and why shouldn't it? Curling is) then I know where the smart money will be.

Farther along I made the sighting the entomologist Ramar had longed for. There it was standing by the road – a lion in spotted pajamas. These are seldom seen because spotted pajamas are hard to find outside the jungle. It was so extraordinary that when I yelled "Leopard!!" the driver slammed on all his brakes. When we got back to the spot of the sighting fifteen minutes later, we saw its tale disappearing into the trees.

So strangely different returning to Nairobi compared to "making it there" the first time. Oddly I, me, a guy who'd stuck to North America almost all his life like he was glued there, was a known entity at the Iqbal Hotel, confirming my suspicion that I had been there before. I arrived that night with no Kenya money but they fed me and gave me a spot on the floor on credit. Yet all my experience of Africa had not unlocked the mystery of the Iqbal toilet.

Next morning I sped to the post office anxious that items sent to general delivery had been returned to sender through my tardiness. Both packages were there and being readied for return.

My investment in Baleisa Hambuli of Isiolo was vindicated. He had shopped well and packaged the bracelets meticulously. They were arranged in neat bundles and the outside of the parcel was sewn up. Irmin and the Aussie, cynical acquaintances from a distant past would have been surprised. Including postage home, the bracelets cost me three dollars each and back in Florida they sold easily for seventeen.

I sent the Tanzanian batiks and oil paintings home by surface mail and the package took six months to arrive, long after I'd forgotten about it. Living in the times we do, I recently googled them to see if I had become wildly rich from my purchase. Turns out Ntegu is known but not valuable - still pinning my hopes on this book.

It will be hard for the reader to imagine, who has not stupidly left his good backpack at home, my joyous reunion with Old Faithful, my lighter than air external frame Himalayan brand backpack from Mom a couple Christmas' back. Immediately I put it on. After toiling so long under the backward beer belly, I preferred my good pack on to having it off, so light did it make me feel, even filled with stuff. The stuff seemed to make it lighter – more like a jetpack than a backpack. I consoled myself with the fine adage, "Better late than never." Look out world. Here I come.

Hitching from Nairobi to Mombasa, on the coast, I got a lift with a truck driver. Since Kenya is touted as the corruption free example for East African countries, I was disillusioned when he was pulled by a cop collecting his tithe because the truck isn't up to snuff.

In place of the pills American truck drivers may pop, he chews an amphetamine-secreting native plant. Sugar is on the dash to ameliorate the bitterness. I tried some and it certainly did taste bad. I thought I was top tier when it came to eating and drinking while driving but he showed me the best way to utilize a Coke bottle. You punch a hole in the top with a screwdriver. The drink can't spill and it lasts the ride.

Chewing this weed is not uncommon in Kenya. I met an expatriated white South African and a Russian on separate occasions. Both claimed to have been forced from their home country. They did nothing but sit outside the Iqbal chewing this weed and smoking cigarets. If I had a country, I'd kick them out, too.

I checked into the Hydro Hotel, Mombasa's equivalent to the Iqbal with less interesting clientele. At night all the streets are lined with people cooking so I sampled off each stand and seldom found something I didn't enjoy. But then what to my wondering eyes did appear but a Swiss bakery! I sat down against the building with one of everything, set my camera bag on the sidewalk beside me and ate it all. In my ensuing euphoria the camera bag made its escape - passport, money and exposed slide film remaining there on the sidewalk, silent as I blissfully walked away. A little while after leaving, my stomach flipped over and I sprinted back in a chocolate panic. My worst fears realized, it was gone. On the plus side, the baker had it. Hard to say which was the emotion more intense.

I attended a Muslim fair where once again my jingoism came to the fore. A huckster was selling a five ball chance at knocking down his apparently invulnerable array of milk bottles; invulnerable, that is, to locals who all throw like little girls. It must take forever to get stoned to death. One imagines the annoying "monkey in the middle" giving 'em raspberries and inflaming their inaccuracy. They probably have to call an intermission so the players can recoup their strength and begin again, during which the target just leaves, explaining the washing's not going to do itself.

So the guy wasn't prepared for a customer who grew up firing baseballs when he wasn't fishing (aka a typical American). After two flings one bottle was standing (they're not arranged to go down all at once like ten-pins). He was shaken but confident that nobody could hit just one bottle. It's the wind-up – and the pitch! When that one disappeared, he stared at me as if I were possessed, and I saw where this could go under the wrong circumstances. He was a very bad sport and refused me my prize, like winning just wasn't fair. He stuck to his guns but my objections attracted a crowd who made him pay. The feeble excuse that I didn't even use all the balls didn't cut the mustard.

Next stop Diani Beach where tourists go to get robbed, as had my old buddy Terry. As would I. Or attacked by a dog. I stayed in Dan Gunn's Campground, next to the Diani Beach Hotel and hung out at the hotel. A fun group was there and we played volleyball and stuff.

One Englishman worked for a London travel agency and a short, stout highly entertaining Cockney worked for, handily, American Express. We were all at a table in Bush Baby's Bar and a big African woman, apparently a prostitute, added herself. Her butt hadn't touched the seat when the Cockney told her to "Get lost." I don't think he could have strapped her in any tighter. A tennis match ensued with grenades in lieu of balls and she gave as good as she got. I admired her fortitude staying put and whacking it right back at him only harder. (To have had a tape recorder.) Seated like she owned the table and always would, not intimidated but inspired by this Cockney, she says, "You short little man, you short fat little man with your short fat little fingers, you must have a short...."

She never did get up from the table, and why would she? After awhile I thought one of them might cross the supposedly fine line between hate and love but I was wrong. Finally he couldn't abide her presence any longer. We all vacated the table, ushered out by her catcalls.

A seventeen year old German boy named Thorsten was staying with his family at the hotel. He looked Angelic and impressed me as being angelic, probably the best German ever and his is a tragic tale. And possibly my fault. Perhaps Germans are the way they are because nature punishes the aberrations.

Tales were rife of bands of Africans armed with pangas (small knives) roaming the beach at night robbing tourists. Stories also abounded of the rifling of caches at hostels and campgrounds. My strategy evolved into carrying all my valuables with me at all times in my camera bag. This included the priceless exposed films of my trip. Someday doing a slide show for friends and family, and sending pictures to the people I had promised seemed my most powerful motives for staying alive.

One morning I walked some miles south on the desolate beach. Sitting on the sand contemplating my navel, I noticed three raggedly dressed African men emerge from the woods. With all the wide beach, they were trudging straight to me, so I stood up to greet them. Having received only kindness from most Africans, I wasn't entirely suspicious of their motives. They walked up to me and I faced them as they pulled out their pangas. One of them said, “Hello, brother,” but I knew this wasn't Arnie.

Martial arts movies are wildly popular in Kenya, eliciting great excitement with every fight scene. I was told later that if you strike a karate pose, muggers will run like diarrhea. This was one case where the good old “Better late than never” didn't hold.

My films in the camera bag cast horror over the situation. This precluded thoughts of anything but how to preserve them. I assumed, being relatively fast and given the enormous incentive, that I could outrun these guys. I made a break for it and got a bad start in the soft sand and a worse finish when a pile of seaweed tripped me up. This shows you how prejudice gets started. Never had I disliked seaweed as I did then. Instantly they had caught up with me, cut the strap on my bag before I hit the ground and three and a half months of slides were theirs; along with money and my camera and some lenses. Bitterly I had just finagled another four hundred dollars from the bank for use on the black market. The SLR was expendable but the films! How to get them back – there's a huge difference in strategy once the goods have changed hands.

The biggest one had the bag. I grabbed for it and missed. Unfortunately I had no experience in defeating three guys but I was willing to try it. As I explained how that really was my bag and not theirs, I was figuring which one to punch first if diplomacy failed. But one of the beach boys had gotten behind me and put his panga point up against my ribs. That was a brand new sensation and soothed me remarkably so I shelved the attack and simply blocked their way from returning to the woods. As in *The Ransom of Red Chief*, they were starting to see what a pain I can be so they solved that problem by dropping films onto the sand as they walked away. This kept me occupied picking them up and stuffing them in my pockets. I never was satisfied though and the fellows lost patience and removed money and camera and handed me the bag with the remaining films, passport (probably the most valuable item) and best lenses in it.

Having glimpsed the abyss of no photos, I was pretty content with losing my camera and money until I remembered the film in the camera with maybe the best sunrise I'd ever snapped. The pirates had progressed down the beach and were starting back into the woods when I renewed pursuit. The English speaking one turned and saw me coming. He shouted, "You don't know what you're dealing with. We could skin you alive right here." Nobody had ever said that to me before and I've always had a real thing about bypassing that procedure. I decided not to push it in favor of sunrises as yet unseen.

After awhile I noticed blood leaking from a small panga wound in my elbow. But what hurt worse, they had taken my wonderful Uganda bark hat.

So I go all through Uganda unscathed and get hijacked in Kenya – naturally. Back at the hotel I related my sad story. A credit to his calling, the Cockney American Express agent loaned me ten bucks instantly. My checks were American Express and worth 2,500 dollars. They were replaced next day in Mombasa no questions asked. It must be routine there. Of course this points up an easy, foolproof way to double your money in those days on arriving in a country with a black market. You find a black marketeer who accepts travelers checks, sell him yours and then report them stolen. Or the reverse order.

Ultimately my response to the theft was petty, feeling about their gain more aggrieved than my loss. I hated how happy they must have been with the cash. Conversely it also bothered me that they would sell the camera for nothing close to its value to me.

Between getting mugged and the hotel, I popped into the police station because I thought it couldn't hurt, so why not. I was wrong about that. Curiously the officers seemed to take extreme measures not to savvy my directions to the crime scene so it was ages before we arrived.

A wee house nestled down the road from the campground where a woman would cook you a meal if you could find her. After dining there the next evening, I visited the hotel and saw a mummy, giving me a horrible flashback to Cairo – but wait – from beneath the bandages rose a pitiful sound - the voice of the German angel Thorsten.

Why, you are asking, had the world been deprived in this way of sweetness and light? I will explain. That evening Thorsten was strolling the beach, sunbeams, moonbeams, bluebirds, elves and unicorn-riding Orthodox Jews cascading about happily in his brain of ambrosia; soon to be joined by two policemen with a dog patrolling the beach supposedly because of my report, although miles from the location. They spotted the celestial being and yelled at him. With my experience fresh in mind Thorsten opted for flight. The savvy cops recognized his criminal intent and let go the dog.

When the dog had done with him, the police arrested Thorsten for being a mugger and dragged his ravaged body down to the station. Instantly I saw how Jesus so effortlessly got his comeuppance. I believe we see this work ethic other places as well, though in reverse. Nothing on this planet looked less like three ragged African beach pirates than that teenager. But I had made a report and they needed to pinch somebody not their associates.

Recreation at Diani Beach was eliminated entirely for Thorsten and for me limited by no surf, no reef and turbid water; but rescuing this was a nearby marine sanctuary, a bit of Indian Ocean protected from any sort of fishing and it was spectacular. At last a use for the snorkeling gear I'd been lugging all over East Africa. I could descend a few feet below the surface, grab ahold of the bottom edge of a huge brain coral and sit there surrounded by fish, big groupers swimming by and schools of different kinds of smaller fishies all around until I had to rise for a breath. Also featured were sparkling tide pools big enough to snorkel in.

But the road beckoned. Irmin Opper had told me of a lovely island off northern Kenya. A Canadian woman from the campground proposed accompanying me there so off we thumbed to Lamu. Two for the road.

At some point a luxury car stopped with the white occupants claiming to be mother and son. Andrew Harpham is the name the young man gave and said he was an artist and they had a house in Mombasa. They seemed pretty nice and offered to safeguard my films until my return to Mombasa, which I would have to do to return to Nairobi. I was so tired of fretting over the films that I handed them over to these strangers. Then at least it was out of my hands. Either I would have the precious films again or I wouldn't and there was nothing for me to do about it. What a relief.

Further along we were waiting at a ferry crossing, a one vehicle at a time affair pulled across with a rope; and here comes the unmistakable handiwork of the patron saint of hitchhikers, my old pal Smurfy. When the ferry arrived at our bank it carried a jeep with two black Kenyans - the very appealing Timothy S.O. Dawa and the more serious-minded David Mangi. To me they became knights errant, people displaying only the tip of the good they're capable of.

Wandering in that pre-internet fog, we were informed by these two medics that it was Jomo Kenyatta's birthday. To honor this occasion, Kenya was hosting a blood drive with all districts competing. They were representing Hola district. They invited us and promised to return to this spot so we could carry on to Lamu.

We visited schools and prisons, soda pop on board to bribe the kids and beer for prisoners. These guys were born to charm blood from people's veins, maybe descended from Transylveinians. Timothy was particularly wonderful with kids. They carried the procured blood all day in an uncooled styrofoam chest and refrigerated it by night.

One morning they argued bitterly with another man over use of a vehicle. He had commandeered it as he was authorized to do but our friends felt they could make better use of it.

We met up with another partner of theirs, setting the scene for the evening motel debate; a fascinating contrast to advanced people, who have tv to watch. I was astounded at the skill displayed. Not that I know anything about it but I got the feeling they would lay waste to any Harvard debating team.

They conducted these matches most respectfully with sharply honed intensity and great fun. They battled with their minds, each a well stocked arsenal. They besieged each other with misdirection, outflanked their opponent with unpredictable logic and sometimes left me behind. At one point the speaker seemed to have hopelessly lost the thread and was just eloquently rambling. But the circuitous manner in which he could express his view was often breathtaking. From five minutes of apparently irrelevant gesticulating and speech making, his entire purpose emerged clear as Kilimanjaro, every word aligning perfectly behind it, and the debater brought down his point on his opponent like a skyscraper toppling onto a fruit stand. Never had I heard a brain sound like this and I listened to them in awe. All of it not in Swahili but the king's English, perhaps in consideration of their audience; and with that lovely Kenya accent. I don't know which language they preferred.

They asked me to supply their next topic and I ripped the scab off a volcano. Kenya's largest tribe, the Kikuyu have adopted colonial ways. They dress English, live in town and eat fish and chips. Meanwhile the Masai wear goat skins, carry long staffs or spears and herd goats like always. They are an embarrassment to the Kikuyu and reviled by the modernistic tribe for their primitive demeanor. In return Masai scorn the Kikuyu for being Oreos.

I proposed, "What do you think about the difference between the way the Masai and the Kikuyu behave?"

One of the medics was Masai by tribe without the goatskin, and another Kikuyu. Both lit up like a supermarket. Here's two orators who could make a great debate out of ugali and they waged war on this topic. I can only say you had to be there. Thanks again Smurfy.

The prison we visited was isolated in the middle of nowhere with a small lake down the hill. I tried fishing from the bank but wading was required. I removed my sneakers and started in but then some virgin repository of good sense in my brain was activated and a hologram of Nancy Reagan's head hovered before me. She looked me in the eye and said, "Just say NO to bilhartzia." So naturally I did. It was terribly frustrating but with her help I chose ignorance of this lake's fishes over death by horrible disease, showcasing advanced judgment that must have developed along the way. Sometimes I couldn't even recognize myself.

Nancy's head may have got loose and floated up to the venue to say "Just say NO to beer" because Timothy and David were striking out. They felt if they could get one inmate to donate, the rest would follow. Finally the promise of a brew overcame one man's wariness of the mysterious procedure and he agreed to swap blood for beer. Soon the intrepid vampires were doing far better than they had dared to hope. On returning from not fishing, I saw prisoners on gurneys hooked contentedly to i.v.'s, awaiting their reward; but Timothy was seething.

Now let's put this in perspective. Whom do you think got the beer? The imprisoned or the butthole in charge? And who were made into liars?

Just then The fat warden and his doltish aide walked in and sauntered around drinking on beers in front of the blood givers who then knew they must be content with Orange Crush and treachery.

It was a sickening display and one too many for Timothy. Beside himself with outrage, he got in the warden's face and told him, "If you must have the beer than at least drink it somewhere else."

I saw the warden and his man sitting in the warden's office joylessly engorging their booty with the insipid, empty faces of two very selfish men. You see I learned in Africa not to refer to disagreeable people always as body parts. And am better for it.

We were in the vicinity of the wild Tana River. In the past year forty Africans had lost an encounter along its banks with a crocodile or a black buffalo. The delta of the Tana River was a fabled place I had learned of since coming to Africa and longed to see. The only way I knew of to reach it was a costly and complicated boat excursion. As I continued to bask in the warmth of fortune's smile, this is exactly where Timothy and David wished to go next. They too pined to see it.

We reached the river via dirt road within sight of the delta. It wasn't particularly spectacular but we got to see it and that completed our lives at the moment. The dauntless medics made the rounds at a nearby village.

Upstream a little ways I tried fly rod in a bend, dropping nymph into eddy. Getting nothing, I caught and skewered a grasshopper which produced a beautiful little silvery catfish. A young girl got the idea then and brought me grasshoppers, always decapitated. She thought that made them better bait but it rendered them useless. Sorry, grasshoppers. Too bad Johnny Kabagambe never taught me "Don't decapitate them."

The Canadian woman donated to the cause. The proposition was debated thoroughly in my head and it was resolved that I needed as much going for me as possible including a full supply of blood; and karma didn't count.

They had collected enough to transfuse a herd of elephants

and I wonder if they won. Back at the ferry crossing Timothy's parting words were, "We like you. You are free people."

Looking back, we surely had great fun as merrily we rode along but it's irksome that I remember none of it. I remember more of Irmin Opper. Maybe only aggravating talk sticks.

Smurfy operates with little room for error, doesn't she? We arrive later at the crossing and none of this happens. Maybe something else but probably not so good. Or maybe it was simply Smurfy's Will and incontrovertible. Either way I keep getting what I can't even know to ask for.

Lamu Island

Arab island, lots of tourists not by Orlando standards, weird singing and bell clanging from temples awakening me at 4:30 every morning. This place is known for woodworking and fabulous doors. They also make dhows. When a fifty or sixty footer is ready, the builder presents a feast to the islanders who in turn pull the ship to water over a log roadway.

Lots of palm trees and sand to grow them. I succeeded around a dock with jigs, catching an interesting kind of grunt and jacks. Swimming at the beach without a partner was tricky as someone always was watching from the dunes for an opening to snatch whatever was left on the sand.

My first order of business, I found an unpopular place to eat called Bathawabba's. I knew this was the place for me on seeing a glass wiped out with a dry rag (looks like my recent use of good sense exhausted the supply). I brought them a small jack, expecting some preparation commensurate with their level of hygiene. Instead I received a taste sensation. It had been coated in munjorno curry powder and cooked in coconut juice. The flavor was so exciting that I bought a coconut squeezing basket and equivalent curry powder to replicate it back home, which I never managed to do. All the other tourists were dining in boring tourist restaurants so I promoted Bathawabba's and soon they had a small Caucasian clientele.

This island has strict codes about where a tourist can stay. I stayed in a somewhat illegal house. An empathetic Englishman loaned me his camera for a day, a great boon as being unable to photograph anything was killing me. A policeman got abusive at the station, saying I was taking pictures in a forbidden place. Probably he was trying to scare some money out of me but I only got belligerent so he gave it up.

Lamu is the place to go having won an academic fellowship or needing to recover from hepatitis. There for both, one pretentious guy said to me pretentiously, “I'm a Fulbright Fellow.”

I took him down a peg. “Oh,” I said with interest, “Does that mean you sell Fuller brushes?”

Got 'im!

After a day of sailing forth and back collecting timber from a couple orders of magnitude larger mangrove trees than I ever saw in Florida, men sail right to their mooring and in an instant drop the sail and stop on a dime. No coasting or motoring in for them.

The Canadian woman remained in Lamu and I returned to the mainland. The rains were coming on strong and the road had turned to mud. I exited the ferry onto probably the last bus for awhile from the ferry landing to the nearest town. We passed one bus already off the road and the spattered passengers trying to push it back on. Then our bus started to slide but luckily we held. I saw elephants, zebras, giraffes and a servil cat. Imagine driving down the road seeing these animals as you would a squirrel. Getting toward Mombasa I caught a mutatu ride. Suddenly an ostrich burst from the bush and raced alongside us, perhaps one I trained up near Lake Turkana. They can have Mars. Africa's different enough for me.

With my heart and all my unexposed slide cannisters in my mouth I arrived in Mombasa and began my hunt for Andrew

Harpham, the rather sickly looking young artist who was custodian of my summer vacation. I found him and his house where predicted and it was a kind of palace overlooking Mombasa Harbor. It had been the right choice.

Noteworthy is a couple sharing the room my second time at the Hydro – a big Dutch woman (and when I say big I mean big and strong. Her windmill didn't need no wind) married to a Masai. In every way she was the antithesis of a Masai woman.

I figured she probably was ruining his life, subjecting him to ridicule from his tribesmen. But then envy is usually the wellspring of ridicule so maybe that's why he was always smiling. This was my first chance to observe a Masai for a period of time and out of his element. I still can picture him lying there exuding contentment. He seemed more at peace than a jellyfish.

On the other hand, the Dutch woman was frustrated that, as with any Masai man, "why" means nothing to him. Truly it is only a crooked letter (now that I think of it, like my parents, who used to tell me that). She never could hear why he had done something. He already did it and moved on, lacking the "why" chromosome. Always, apparently, looking ahead - but not knowing why. At this writing I wonder if they do know why and it's handy to let the women think they don't. And I wonder if this odd couple still are together.

She asked him what he would have done seeing the men robbing me on the beach. He said he would have come to my aid. But he didn't know why.

And I'm pretty sure he didn't know why he didn't know why he didn't know why.

I'd been advised to take the train second class from Mombasa to Nairobi so I did and it was great. The second class cars are gorgeous old fashioned relics made entirely of wood. There I was, leaning out from the platform between cars as we chugged around a curve in the East African night. And not a chance of getting eaten by anything. Unless I fell off. Perish the thought.

Amazingly I ran into Thorsten and his family in the dining car, heading for Nairobi and then the fatherland. Eventually I would see in my address notepad the name Thorsten Bauer and wonder who he was. I put it together when a bald German in his twenties visited me in Orlando. He had become a veterinarian of all things, further testimony to his angelic nature; and lots of fun. He stripped down to his briefs in the Publix parking lot where I photographed him posing by his car and looking more cherubic than ever.

Lamu

OUT of AFRICA

And then it was time to go. Time to make more money, get those slides developed and have that slide show. Was the fun over? Not quite yet. The only question was the usual one: How little can it cost me?

By requiring bank receipts equivalent to the cost, the Kenya government makes it hard to use black market shillings for an airline ticket. But rules need not apply everywhere. I had heard of Crocodile Travel, not only for crocodiles. After some searching, I found this handy place in Nairobi atop a fire escape on the back of an old building. The portly white man at his desk in the tiny room assured me bank receipts would be no problem. When his customers actually *have* bank receipts, he saves some for his other customers. He pulled out a drawer stuffed with them. Voila! Better yet he could sell me a discounted ticket on Aeroflot all the way to London via Moscow for a hundred and sixty-two dollars. That sounded fine. Plus it turned out to be a lot more fun than you expect an airline flight to be.

The plane was big and so were the stewardesses. There were thirteen other passengers, seemed kind of odd. One was a big headed classic looking Russian writer or something, straight out of Dr. Zhivago. There was a highly dissatisfied Afganny, a couple prissy girls, a few others and us; us being me and some other guys I just met. The Afganny was angrily at the Russian the whole flight.

Paint was peeling off the interior, stewardesses were strong, stern, unsmiling plainly uniformed Russian women and the bounty at mealtime was shocking. Supper included not only some pretty good looking broiled fish but a sizable hunk of red meat as well. Food over smiles any day.

I think it all started with one guy getting his dessert smashed and then trying to get someone else's. That might have been me, but odds are it was somebody else. Next thing we're wrestling in the aisles, actually diving over the seats at each others' desserts. I'm pretty sure no one got to eat his or anybody else's dessert. They all got disintegrated. That was the shame of it.

We stopped in Odessa but were not allowed off the plane. Maybe our reputation preceded us. Approaching the Moscow airport, we watched our connecting flight take off to the left. That was alright because that meant two free days in the airport hotel *in Russia,* a country of my ancestors, and free food. Still smiling, fortune seemed to be ushering me all the way home.

We were restricted to hot dog and cold cuts Heaven by guards posted at the hotel doors. This Indian- English kid from the plane and I crashed a wedding party twice. Each time we were eagerly welcomed by the celebrants and sternly banished by a stalwart older woman. Also I got drinking with a drunk Russian Air Force guy. Drunker than I, he kept trying very hard to express something to me as we sat at the bar, appearing to strain his whole brain and his face but he never could put it together. It seemed very important to him and he was saddened by the failure. At this same bar I was invited to drink champagne with some Russian girls who subsequently got angry because I didn't buy *them* any champagne. On principle I had already found the black market, changing money with a waiter, so I had some rubles.

The women working in the hotel were middle-aged and tried to be very cold toward us but I suspected it was an act. I performed my foolproof test. In view of a couple of them I tried to sew up the hole in the knee of my jeans. In no time one of them had ripped it all from me and performed an act of kindness, to me and herself who wouldn't have to endure the spectacle any longer.

Having shown her true colors, she never was able to be quite so hard after that.

The morning of our scheduled departure for London, the Indian-English guy and I decided to see Moscow. We strode right past the guard, hopped on the first bus we saw and we were off.

Many people, naysayers, might say that wasn't a smart thing to do in the overall scheme of things (once again, not a big picture guy). But we had a plan and so far it was working. Somehow we were walking around Moscow eating Russian ice creams, my buddy unceasingly flirting with Russian girls who were consistently horrified by it. I couldn't see why. He seemed charming to me.

Against all odds we made it to Red Square where we met some American girls there legitimately who made us wish we were staying longer and then we figured we should get back to the hotel. Before long we were hopelessly lost in the Moscow subway system. And of all the arrogance, nobody around there seemed to speak English. Time was doing what it does best - ticking away. Finally we found someone who could direct us. I was sorely tempted to light out for the Crimea where my father came from, someplace I always wanted to see. The onset of winter and a hole in my jeans held me back. It might have been a whole 'nother adventure that I didn't have. Or maybe just miserable and then arrested. Who knows?

By the time we get back, the other passengers have been taken to the airplane. My pal immediately storms the desk where, enraged, he demands to know why we weren't informed. The girl behind the desk shakes her head in amusement and says, "We know where you were. You went to town, didn't you?"

He keeps denying it when it has become ridiculous to deny it and it seems he ought to stop. Then a more mature woman reminiscent of Natasha Fatale appears and says with forbearance, "You can go to the plane but you must never speak of your experience." It sounded good to me. Probably they were quite relieved we had returned and no one would be served by making something out of it.

More fun on the flight to London. One of my air-buddies offered a lift but I phoned Tim and Sheila, the English couple that didn't seem like a couple that I had met on the plane to Nairobi. They picked me up at the airport.

Tim is a school teacher and he has a friend who considers himself a "disrupter." In high school his friend would stand up suddenly on a table and start making all kinds of noises. When the teacher scolded him for this, he'd protest, "I'm a disrupter and that's what I'm doin'! I'm disruptin'."

In the course of hanging out together, Tim told me that Sheila had a roving eye or two and he was hanging in there being tormented. That fit with my impression from my first visit when it seemed to me she treated him coldly.

On the night of my departure Sheila alone drove me to the airport. I guess the old American charisma was working because she made some very interesting remarks. She was naturally sensational looking but perhaps with misplaced loyalty I refused to add to *The Torment of Timothy Talbott.*

And then I came home sweet home and that's the end of my summer vacation.

Well there's always more.

The last plane ride of my trip got me within two hundred-fifty miles of home. They call it Miami. I don't know why. I don't know whose ami it is but it's certainly not mine. I was very excited because I also loved coming home from a trip. I was standing thumb out at an intersection away from the terminal because I had failed to ingratiate myself with the proper people on the airplane (no ride offers). But this too would work in my favor, for the drama I got to witness. A black man and a white man played their roles to the hilt.

From my time in New York City I had the impression that the

black employees of the subway system had a chip on their shoulders for Whitey. The black man reminded me of them. The white man was real white looking and all dressed up in a three piece suit with someplace to go.

The black man was piloting an airport bus and the white man was crossing an intersection on foot. The white man was about to alter the course of the black man's life.

The white man, we'll call him Whitey, was heading for the corner I was occupying and the driver was bearing down on him not slowing, intent on cutting off his adversary. Whitey was equally determined to make the bus stop, slowing his pace to be sure he was right in front of the bus when it reached the crossing. Each knew what the other was about. Whitey won.

At the last moment the bus driver slammed on the brakes and burning rubber, stopped not ten feet from the pedestrian and lined up perfectly with him for the kill, cursing. Whitey took two triumphant steps, barely clearing himself from the direct path of the bus. At this moment entered the wild card. This was the driver of the next bus, following close behind the first bus, unaware of the game, with no time to hit his brakes. I watched bus #2 slam into bus #1 at full speed drilling it through the intersection, practically grazing the dressed-up white guy as he stood there thunderstruck. Had he held his position in front of the stopped bus a couple seconds longer... I was glad I didn't see that. They'd never get the wrinkles out the suit. He stood there in the road and looked at me and there was complete understanding between us. I knew exactly what that man to whom I never had spoken was thinking.

At least one bus driver lost his job right then but nobody lost a life. Yet. I eased on down the road before I could be spotted as a witness.

Epilogue

About two weeks after getting back, I was in Melbourne peddling laser prints. Feeling weak, I went to a park by the ocean and slept for a couple hours on the grass. Waking up weaker and feverish, I started the eighty mile trip back to Orlando, stopping at the Pop Shoppe to sell a couple pictures.

I felt no better for a couple weeks. In fact I forgot what "good" meant. Mom took me to the hospital where they ran tests and were flummoxed. The doctor said he'd never seen such a high white blood cell count. Then my poop turned gray, I turned yellow and they knew what I had. A legacy of Bathawabba's, I'd wager.

A few years later thumbing around New Zealand, I would look up Terry Johnstone at his parents' house in Napier. He told me of his trip south on Lake Tanganyika on a boat jammed with the usual suspects and his parallel experience in South Africa of getting picked up by white people to rescue him from contact with black ones. I asked how it went sending the photo to the nice woman we met exiting the Ngong Hills. I was sorry to learn that he who so mightily had touted his New Zealand integrity had never intended to fulfill our promise. He was surprised I had expected him to. Of all the new things I encountered on my summer vacation, this is the most difficult to understand.

"But you were happy enough to get the water, weren't you?" I pointed out. I felt bad thinking of her waiting for the marvelous image that never would arrive and angry because he had made a liar out of me too.

Oh yeah ...

Most people don't go to Africa so why did I and why, out of the whole continent, Kenya? And out of all the lakes, why Turkana? Turned out there was an instigator for all this other than my great fallback, random chance – the subconscious mind.

To appreciate this, the reader should know, if he hasn't noticed yet, that fishing can be a strong impulse, without doubt my main genetic force. It kicked in at the age of four in New York when suddenly I started begging my parents to take me to the beach to go fishing and it hasn't abated.

The reader may recall my determination to reach Lake Turkana. Once I got going, nothing was going to stop me, even lack of gasoline. To divine the source of this drive, we must return in time to the small living room in a house in Orlando, Florida, ten years before the far away and auspicious birth of one Agostino Llowoi. Sitting lotus style on the plush carpet is a boy about the age Agostino will be when they eventually meet,

As closely as he can without going blind, he is watching a black and white documentary on a little known lake in a fabled place called Kenya. It shows natives carrying the largest perch he'd never heard of. The lure of this lake where practically nobody ever had been is irresistible to his genes and he literally aches to fish in Lake Rudolph, also steeped in the heartbreaking knowledge that he has equal chance of angling on the moon. I had long ago forgotten all this.

While recuperating from hepatitis in the same Orlando house, I looked up Lake Turkana in the encyclopedia (that's right, e-n-c-y-c-l-o p e d i a). Strangely, our 1956 edition of The World Book made no mention of Lake Turkana, just as if I had dreamed it. Research in a more current source gave me a revelation that about knocked me out the chair and stood me straight up: I read that before Kenyan independence in 1975 Lake Turkana had been named after some German explorer named Rudolph. With this name the long dormant memory of the documentary and my longing popped into my head like a jack-in-the-box and then I knew why I went to Africa. It was simply the man being true to the boy. Even now, reading the name Lake Rudolph returns to me the feeling I had when I was watching the tv. I'm sure glad the boy was so persistent.

People so inclined might even suggest that Agostino Lowoi had been my spirit child there to meet me.

Speaking of that imp, ever since then I have wondered how my young friend has fared and if indeed he still was faring, harsh landscape that he was part of. I don't do much with "social media" but, because of putting together this story, it occurred to me, what the heck I could check facebook. One in a million shot. Those odds finally paid off. There, right after the law firm of Lo and Behold was the name Agostino Moru Lowoi. Similar name, different cat? Profile said he was a Turkana, runs a safari company out of Nairobi – fifty years old, the right age - it was him – with a boy same age as he was when I knew him - seems to be a pattern. We had a Facebook reunion. I may never ridicule Farcebook again. He answered some questions I've wondered about since I was there. One of which was did he eventually participate in the rite of passage we witnessed. He says that in their pastoralist community, culture transcends religion and government law. It is called the Asapan and it is their law to do it. He is now an elder and he could not have achieved that status without it.

Wrote Agostino, "It was many years back when I was only 11 years old. I had no idea what I looked like then. Then you found me again. I don't think this was coincidence. I think it was God working on reuniting us."

Rites of male passage seem to be in the dna – The Bar Mitzvah, the Catholic Confirmation, the Turkana Asapan, etc. Many Americans without culture fall back on their son's first legal beer. Pathetic but still it draws a line of before and after. Now you're a man, Son. Drink beers at will.

Time flies when you're having fun if free time is a precious and finite commodity. Open ended it reins in nicely. In a rut the hour hand sweeps while you stand still. Naught happened and it's your birthday again. Felt like two months but it's been a year. You don't need Einstein to turn that around. I think I'm out a couple months so I call home but people there think I just left. That's because it's only been two weeks. Bingo! And it works the same looking back. I highly recommend it.

If you wish to consider your future self, when you take off keep a journal. When I found my measley 13 day diary I saw it was full of stuff I had forgotten and then I realized how much was lost from the rest of the trip by not writing it down.

Lastly, the key to writing a book can be surviving the research. You can bet your dirty socks some great stories went untold for inattention to that detail. Me, I've always been lucky.

This is and always was for the people I wish had been there

Michael Emor says,

"The end."